Build and Repair with Concrete

The Complete Do-It-Yourself Manual

THIRD EDITION

The QUIKRETE® Companies

The QUIKRETE® Companies
2987 Clairmont Road, Suite 500
Atlanta, GA 30329

www.quikrete.com

Acknowledgements
We are grateful to the following organizations for their cooperation in pro-
viding photographs and other information for the book: Portland Cement
Association, The Brick Institute of America.

Library of Congress Catalog Card Number: 92-81730

Library of Congress Cataloging in Publication Data

Build and repair with concrete—3rd edition.

    Includes index.
    1. Concrete construction—Amateurs' manuals.
I. The QUIKRETE® Companies.
TA682.42.B85   1986   693'.5   85-30139
ISBN 0-937558-19-2

02 01 00   10 9 8 7
Printed in the United States of America.

This book is dedicated to James Eugene Winchester, chairman of the board of The QUIKRETE® Companies, for his leadership, dedication, and vision in the packaged concrete industry.

A special thanks is also extended to all QUIKRETE® manufacturers for their much-needed help and cooperation in bringing this book to completion.

Contents

Preface

More and more of today's homeowners are taking an active role in the upkeep of their homes and property. And although the average do-it-yourselfer won't hesitate to pick up a hammer or paintbrush, a surprising number of people have the notion that concrete and masonry work is much too difficult and best left to professionals. The QUIKRETE® Companies have written this book to show that you don't have to be a professional mason to produce outstanding results with concrete. By using quality masonry products and following proven techniques, professional results can be achieved. Whether you want to lay a simple concrete slab, build an elaborate garden fountain, or repair a damaged concrete surface, this book will show you how to plan the job and how to complete it successfully.

Introduction

Concrete is made by mixing four ingredients together in proper proportions: portland cement; fine aggregate (usually sand); coarse aggregate (usually gravel or crushed stone); and clean, potable water. A mix of cement, sand, and water, without the coarse aggregate, is called sand mix and is used as a strong finishing or topping material in some projects and repairs.

Mortar mix consists of special masonry cement, fine sand, and other additives that provide the workability and stickiness needed when laying up brick, block, tile, etc.

Special fibers, fiberglass, vinyl resins, powdered polymers, latex emulsions, and other additives are often blended with cement, sand, and aggregate to form unique concretes, mortars, grouts, wall coatings, and repair products. Such specialty products often have distinct characteristics, such as fast initial or final setting times, high early or final strength, high tensile or compressive strength, water stopping ability, or increased resistance to cracking and chipping. Specialty products are often intended for specific jobs or types of applications. Take the time to match the correct product to the job, and know the product's properties and limitations before you begin. Finally, manufacturer's instructions are designed to ensure you get the most out of the products you use. Read and follow their advice.

The aggregates, fibers, and additives in concrete and mortar mixes are called inert ingredients, while the cement and water are known as active ingredients. When water is added to the mix, a chemical reaction called hydration occurs between the cement and water in the mix. It is this hydration process that causes the concrete to harden. If water is lost from the mix through evaporation, hydration stops and the concrete does not reach its full strength. Concrete must be kept moist (cured) during the initial hydration process. Mortar used in masonry work is not normally cured in this manner, but it is equally important to use properly mixed mortar with the right working consistency. Like poorly cured concrete, mortar that is too wet or dry will give less than ideal results.

Concrete can be formed into practically any shape, with a variety of finishes, textures, and colors. Since it is made only of inorganic materials, concrete is impervious to decay, termites, and rodents. It is noncombustible, and when properly placed, concrete is usually not affected by heat and cold. These extraordinary properties combine to give concrete durability, good appearance, and long-term economy that few building materials can match.

The same desirable characteristics appear in masonry work as well. Hundreds of styles, textures, and sizes of brick, block, stone, tile, and specialty products allow amateur and professional masons to create and build thousands of practical, beautiful projects that will last not only for years, but for generations.

SECTION I:
QUIKRETE®
PROJECTS

What do an exposed aggregate patio, a brick tree well, a block retaining wall, and a shuffleboard court have in common? They all can be made by using QUIKRETE® concrete and mortar mixes. In this section, we'll show you how easy it is to make these as well as many other interesting and useful projects. You'll learn step-by-step how to add beauty and value to your home and property. You can do it—with QUIKRETE®.

BEFORE YOU BEGIN

Section III of this book contains information on selecting concrete and masonry products, estimating material needs, and working with tools safely. The basics of zoning laws and building codes are also discussed. It is highly recommended that you review Section III before beginning any project listed in Sections I and II. Obtain approval from local building authorities prior to any construction requiring their approval.

There are also other steps you can take to ensure the best result possible. Plan thoroughly. Think the project through; work within your skill level; and pay attention to details, such as subgrade preparation and formwork construction.

Know your physical limitations. Concrete is heavy, and once mixed, all concrete finishing work becomes a race against time. So mix and work at a comfortable pace, breaking the job down into smaller sections if needed. Have plenty of helpers on hand for larger jobs.

Work when the weather is favorable, and always cure the concrete using one of the methods outlined below.

Curing Concrete

Curing is one of the most important steps in concrete construction. Proper curing increases the strength and durability of concrete, and a poor curing job can ruin an otherwise well-done project. Proper water content and temperature are essential for good curing. In near-freezing temperatures, the hydration process slows considerably. When weather is too hot, dry, or windy, water is lost by evaporation from the concrete, and hydration stops, resulting in finishing difficulties and shrinkage cracks. The ideal circumstances for curing are ample moisture and moderate temperature and wind conditions.

Moist-curing is done in several ways: by covering the surface with wet burlap; by keeping the surface wet with a lawn sprinkler; or by sealing the concrete surface with plastic sheeting, waterproof paper, or a curing compound to prevent moisture loss.

If burlap is used, it should be free of chemicals that could weaken or discolor the concrete. New burlap should be washed before use. Place it when the concrete is hard enough to withstand surface damage and sprinkle it periodically to keep the concrete surface continuously moist.

Water curing with lawn sprinklers, nozzles, or soaking hoses must be continuous to prevent interruption of the curing process.

Curing with plastic sheets is convenient. They must be laid flat, thoroughly sealed at joints, and anchored carefully along edges. But curing with plastic can cause patchy discoloration in colored concrete. For colored concrete, chemical curing compounds are recommended.

Curing should be started as soon as possible and should continue for a period of five days in warm weather (70°F or higher) or seven days in cooler weather (50°F to 70°F). The temperature of the concrete must not be allowed to fall below 50°F during the curing period.

Pigmented or non-pigmented curing compounds, as well as cure and seal compounds, provide the easiest and most convenient method of curing. These compounds are applied by spraying soon after the final finishing operation. The surface should be damp, but not wet. Complete coverage is essential.

QUIKRETE® Acrylic Concrete Cure & Seal is a specially developed water-repellent formula that not only cures freshly placed concrete but also seals new and old concrete surfaces.

Use of curing compounds is not recommended during late fall in northern climates on surfaces where deicers will be used to melt ice and snow. Using curing compounds at that time may prevent proper air-drying of the concrete, which is necessary to enhance its resistance to damage caused by deicers.

Working in Cold and Hot Weather

Ideally, concrete work should be done well in advance of cold weather. When placed during temperate weather, it is not necessary to take special precautions to prevent the subgrade and concrete from freezing, and there is sufficient time for the concrete to develop strength to resist freezing and thawing and chemical deicers. However, a good concrete job can be done in colder weather if the correct methods are carefully followed.

Do not place concrete on frozen ground. Straw mats, loose straw coverings, and similar materials can be used to keep the earth from freezing prior to placing the concrete. Check over the site and forms, and remove any accumulation of frost or ice.

Remember, proper hardening of concrete occurs when the temperature of the mix falls between 50°F and 70°F. If the temperature falls below 50°F, you should heat the mixing water or use hot water from a garden hose.

When there is danger of freezing, concrete should be kept warm during curing. Insulating blankets, or 12" to 24" of dry straw, covered with canvas, waterproof paper, or plastic sheeting to keep it dry and in place can be used. The effectiveness of the protection can be checked by placing a thermometer under the covering. Slab edges and corners are most vulnerable to freezing.

QUIKRETE® Thermo-Lube® is a calcium-base liquid with special rust inhibitors. It is added to concrete and mortar during cold weather to help accelerate the set before freezing can occur.

In very hot weather, steps must be taken to keep the concrete sufficiently cool and to prevent rapid loss of surface moisture: (1) dampen the subgrade and forms before pouring; (2) minimize the finishing time required by having sufficient manpower on hand; (3) erect sunshades and windbreaks; (4) use temporary coverings, such as wet burlap or plastic sheeting, during the finishing procedure; (5) use light mist sprays periodically to prevent excessive evaporation from the concrete; and (6) start the curing process as soon as possible, using continuous wet methods or curing compounds. During very hot, dry weather, plan to place and finish concrete during the cooler, early morning or late evening hours.

Layout Basics for Slabs and Footers

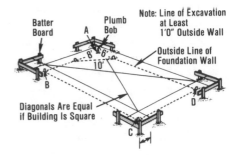

Note: Line of Excavation at Least 1'0" Outside Wall

Batter Board

Plumb Bob

A

Outside Line of Foundation Wall

B

Diagonals Are Equal if Building Is Square

C

D

The first step in placing large concrete slabs, patios, driveways, etc., is to stake out the area using the 3-4-5 triangular method. This method ensures square, true corners on square and rectangular surfaces; and any multiple of this ratio, such as 6-8-10 or 9-12-15, will give the same result. Always use a line level to ensure all lines strung are level. After staking out the area, double-check for squareness by measuring the diagonals between opposite corners. They should be equal.

Slab or Patio Perimeter

When deeper trenches must be dug for wall and foundation footers, it is best to lay out batter boards. Batter boards are set back from the actual work area so they are not disturbed by digging and construction. They also serve as a record of all important locations, such as trench and footer dimensions and the location of the outer edge of the finished wall. To lay out batter boards:

1. Lay out the perimeter of the project by accurately driving stakes at the corners. About 5' outside these

stakes, drive 1" × 4" stakes and construct batter boards as shown. Because the trench must be at least 3' wide to allow room to work, batter boards should be 4' to 5' long.

2. Transfer the building lines to the batter boards by dangling a plumb bob over the outer edge of each corner stake while stretching a length of line between batter boards. This is best done as a two-person operation.

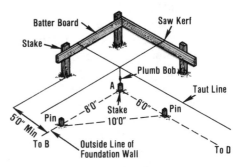

Batter Board

Saw Kerf

Stake

Plumb Bob

A

Taut Line

Pin

8'0"   6'0"

Pin

Stake

50" Min

10'0"

To B

Outside Line of Foundation Wall

To D

3. With the outside corner dimensions marked out on the batter boards, measure over the required distances to record the position of footer and trench edges. Cut small saw kerfs in

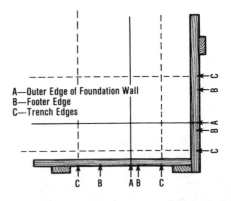

A—Outer Edge of Foundation Wall
B—Footer Edge
C—Trench Edges

C   B   A B   C

the batter boards at these positions so that lines can be accurately strung and restrung whenever needed.

4. After digging the trench, a plumb bob can be used to transfer dimensions for footer forms and final wall positions.

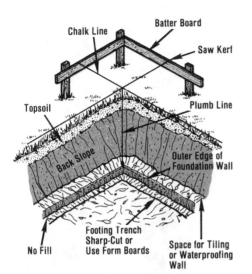

Chalk Line
Batter Board
Saw Kerf
Topsoil
Plumb Line
Back Slope
Outer Edge of Foundation Wall
Footing Trench Sharp-Cut or Use Form Boards
No Fill
Space for Tiling or Waterproofing Wall

Concrete Sidewalks and Small Slabs

Tools and Materials

QUIKRETE® 5000 is the ideal choice for applications requiring high early strength. Because it gains strength quickly, it is ideal for cold weather applications. QUIKRETE® 5000 achieves 5,000 psi after 28 days.

QUIKRETE® Fiber-Reinforced Concrete Mix eliminates the need for wire mesh reinforcement. It also offers increased resistance to surface cracking and chipping.

QUIKRETE® Concrete Mix is a good general-purpose mix for sidewalk and slab work.

QUIKRETE® All-Purpose Gravel or crushed stone (if needed)

T-square, measuring tape, mason's line, level, pickax, shovel, rake, tamper, hammer or half-hatchet,

Tools and Materials (continued)

saw, screed, darby or bull float, hand float, finishing trowel, bricklayer's trowel, edger, and jointer

Forming lumber, stakes, and nails

Wire mesh or rebar (if needed)

Expansion joint material (as needed)

Wheelbarrow and power mixer (recommended) or masonry hoe

Curing materials

Private walks leading to the front entrance of a home should be 3′ to 4′ wide. Service walks connecting to back or side entrances can be 2′ to 3′ wide. Sidewalks should be at least 4″ in thickness. Simple slabs for small foundations, bases, etc., normally are 4″ to 6″ thick, depending on the load they must bear.

Slope the walk away from buildings to provide proper drainage. A slope of 1/4″ per foot is generally recommended, but check local codes and conditions.

SITE PREPARATION

1. Stake out the area for the walk or slab, using a T square, measuring tape, and twine. Use a line level to ensure proper placement and slope of lines.

2. Remove the sod and soil to the desired depth. Remember to account for the width of the forming lumber.

3. Nail and stake the forms in place. You may have to dig a slight trench to set the forms at the correct height.

4. Backfill against the forms to ensure stability.

5. Use the level to check for proper slope. Notice that when held level, the right end of the level is about 1/2″ above the outside form, indicating a slight slope away from the building.

6. Tamp the subbase firm; then check for proper form depth, here 4″.

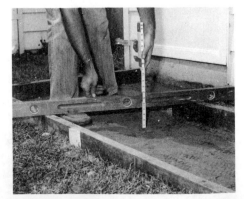

Options

For larger jobs, or in areas of poor drainage, dig to a greater depth and add several inches of QUIKRETE® All-Purpose Gravel or crushed stone to the subbase.

When QUIKRETE® Concrete Mix is used, it may be desirable to add wire mesh reinforcement to the form. Support the mesh on small stones so it is suspended at the midpoint in the slab.

MIXING AND PLACEMENT

1. Add approximately 3/4 of the expected amount of mixing water to the mixer. Turn on the power mixer, and add the QUIKRETE® Fiber-Reinforced Concrete, QUIKRETE® 5000 or Concrete Mix. Add more water as needed to obtain a plastic-like consistency. Do not exceed mixer capacity. **Note:** QUIKRETE® concrete mixes can also be mixed manually in a wheelbarrow or a mortar box.

2. Dampen the subgrade before making the pour. Note the use of a splash board to help direct the flow.

3. Spread the concrete throughout the form, working it in tight against corners and edges.

4. Strike off the concrete level with the top of the forms using the screed board. Fill in any low spots as you work. Several passes may be needed.

5. Float the concrete surface smooth, using a wooden or metal float or darby. Swing the tool in circles, holding the leading edge of the tool up slightly to keep it from digging into the concrete. Float the entire slab. Stop floating when the entire slab is fairly smooth and the float leaves no visible marks. All stone and gravel in the mix should have been worked below the surface.

6. Cut the concrete away from the forms by running an edging tool along the forms to compact the slab edges.

7. Using a straight piece of lumber as a guide, cut 1″ control joints into the slab every 6′ to 8′ using a grooving tool.

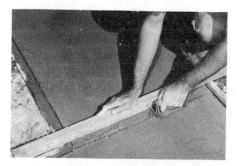

Note: When a coarse finish is desired for nonslip footing, floating, edging, and grooving may be the only steps performed. When a denser, smoother finish is required, the surface is troweled once or several times with a stainless steel trowel. Troweling takes place after the surface moisture has evaporated from the surface and the concrete has lost its sheen. This setting time may vary greatly with weather conditions and the moisture content of the mix, from 30 minutes to several hours. Thirty minutes to an hour is average in most cases.

8. Once the concrete has set up, swing the trowel in the same circular pressing and polishing motion that was used in floating. Continue working until the surface is smooth and dense. You may wish to allow the concrete to continue to harden and then trowel once more for the densest possible finish. After troweling, redo edges and grooves.

9. Properly cure the concrete with Acrylic Concrete Cure & Seal. After the concrete has hardened sufficiently (48 hours or so) carefully remove the forms.

For Best Results

Use double head nails for easy form stripping.

Make curved forms using 1/4" hardboard plywood, kerfed lumber, or sheet metal.

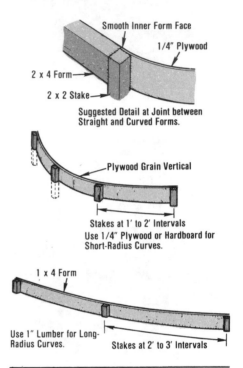

Smooth Inner Form Face

1/4" Plywood

2 x 4 Form

2 x 2 Stake

Suggested Detail at Joint between Straight and Curved Forms.

Plywood Grain Vertical

Stakes at 1' to 2' Intervals
Use 1/4" Plywood or Hardboard for Short-Radius Curves.

1 x 4 Form

Use 1" Lumber for Long-Radius Curves.   Stakes at 2' to 3' Intervals

JOINTS IN SLAB WORK

A concrete slab has low tensile strength and is subject to cracking unless steps are taken to prevent it. To help control stress buildup and the cracking it causes, three types of joints are used in concrete work.

Control joints induce cracking at the base of the control joint, rather than across the face of the slab. They can be hand tooled in fresh concrete or sawn into hardened concrete. Control joints should penetrate roughly 1/4 of the slab thickness and be spaced every 6' to 8' in 4"-thick slab work. Wide driveways and patios may require longitudinal control joints down their centers.

Expansion joints help dissipate the expansion and contraction forces that pass between adjoining structures. They are made by installing a resilient, bituminous fiber strip wherever concrete meets an

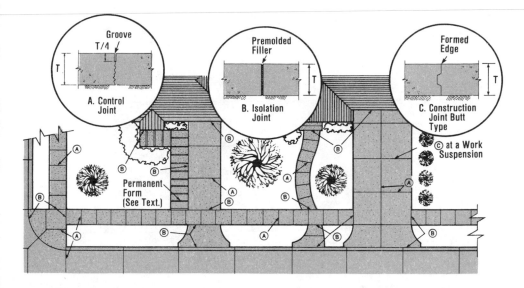

A. Control Joint

Groove
T/4
T

B. Isolation Joint

Premolded Filler
T

C. Construction Joint Butt Type

Formed Edge
T

© at a Work Suspension

Permanent Form (See Text.)

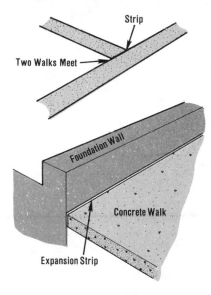

Two Walks Meet

Strip

Foundation Wall

Concrete Walk

Expansion Strip

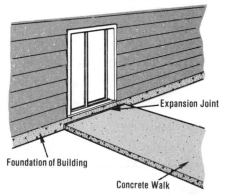

Expansion Joint

Foundation of Building

Concrete Walk

existing structure, such as a foundation, wall, or other slab. Expansion joints should also be installed when concrete is placed around posts, pillars, or other major protrusions.

Construction joints are inserted where concrete placement is stopped for 30 minutes or more or along the perimeter of the day's work. Construction joints are located and built to act as control joints. Install a lumber bulkhead across the form, place concrete to this point, and finish its leading edge with your jointing tool. When work is resumed, remove the bulkhead, place the adjoining section of concrete, and finish the second edge to complete the control joint.

On level, stable ground, simple butt joints are fine for 4"-thick slabs. For thicker slabs, or work on unstable bases, use the tongue and groove type construction joint illustrated below. It will help tie the slabs together and keep them level with each other.

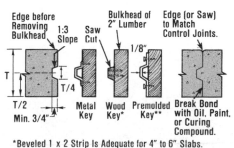

Edge before Removing Bulkhead

1:3 Slope

Saw Cut

Bulkhead of 2" Lumber

1/8"

Edge (or Saw) to Match Control Joints.

T
T/4
T/2
Min. 3/4"

Metal Key

Wood Key*

Premolded Key**

Break Bond with Oil, Paint, or Curing Compound.

*Beveled 1 x 2 Strip Is Adequate for 4" to 6" Slabs.
**May Be Left in Slab Permanently by Tacking Lightly to Bulkhead.

Gallery of Slab Projects

Concrete slabs provide a strong, level base for countless items inside and outside the home. Here are just a few ideas to get you thinking.

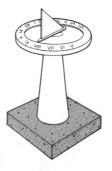

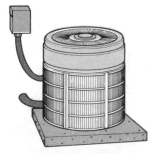

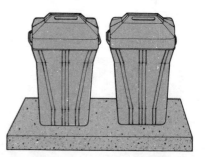

Shuffle-board Court

Shuffleboard is a popular pastime for people of all ages, and with QUIKRETE® Fiber-Reinforced Concrete or QUIK-RETE® Concrete Mix it's easy to make your own shuffleboard court for your backyard.

You'll need a long, narrow area; an official shuffleboard court is 52' long and 6' wide, although it can be as small as 28' long and 3' wide.

Once you've chosen a good spot for the court, it is simply a matter of building the forms and pouring a concrete slab. Work the concrete with a steel trowel to produce a smooth, hard finish. When the concrete has cured for 3 to 4 days, coat the surface with QUIKRETE® Acrylic Concrete Cure & Seal. This will make the surface smooth enough to accommodate the wooden discs. When the sealer has dried, paint on the lines and numbers as shown in the illustration.

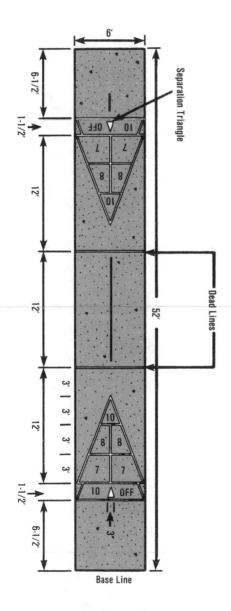

Footers for Walls

Regardless of the type of masonry material you are using to build the wall, concrete is the material of choice for the footer. A typical footer is twice the width of a wall and equal in depth to the wall's width. The footer should rest on a 6" gravel base set below the frost line. Check with your local building department for the exact depth of the frost line in your area and for any local specifications concerning the footer design for the job you have in mind.

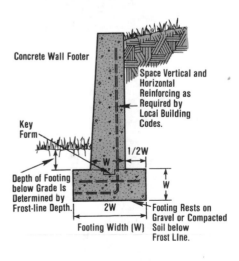

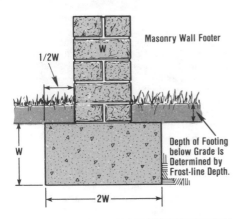

Masonry Wall Footer

1/2W

W

W

2W

Depth of Footing below Grade Is Determined by Frost-line Depth.

Tools and Materials

QUIKRETE® 5000 High Early Strength Concrete Mix or QUIKRETE® Concrete Mix

QUIKRETE® All-Purpose Gravel or crushed stone

Pickax, square-faced shovel, tamper, saw, screed, and level

Rebar, forming lumber, and stakes

CONSTRUCTING FOOTER FORMS

1. Lay out the footer location with batter boards as described on page 4. If the soil is firm enough to hold its shape when filled with wet concrete, consider making an earth form by digging to the correct depth and other dimensions with a square-faced shovel.

2. Firmly compact the soil using a tamper, and add 6″ of QUIKRETE® All-Purpose Gravel or crushed stone to the base to ensure good drainage.

3. Screed guides, leveled and staked at the correct height, will help in striking off concrete in earth forms. After the screeding pass, these guides are removed and the gaps filled with extra concrete and leveled with a trowel.

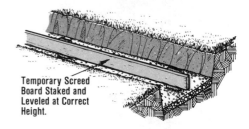

Temporary Screed Board Staked and Leveled at Correct Height.

4. In loose soils, construct strong wooden forms using sturdy lumber, stakes, and nails. Form boards must be parallel and level.

5. Place steel reinforcement bars 1/3 up from the base of the footer.

6. If the footer is to be the base of a poured concrete wall, install a keyway form as shown. This keyway will help tie together the footer and wall.

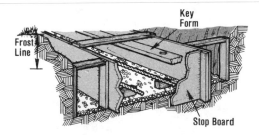

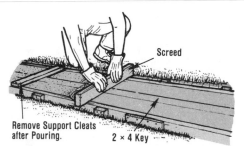

7. On slopes, construct a stepped footing to minimize the amount of concrete used. Stepped forms should rise no more than 2' per step and overlap at least 2' at each step. The same step principle can be used for earth forms.

2. Screed the concrete level. If steel reinforcement is needed for the poured wall, insert it at this time. Predrilled holes in the keyway form make this an easy task. Remove the keyway form as soon as the concrete has set up sufficiently to hold its shape.

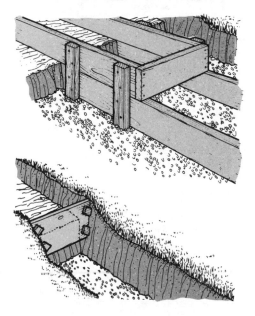

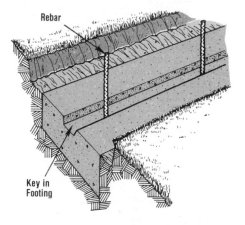

3. Cover the footer and allow it to cure for at least 3 to 4 days before removing forms and continuing work.

POURING THE FOOTING

1. Oil the forms with clean motor oil or a concrete release agent. Mix and pour the QUIKRETE® Concrete, working from one end of the form to the other. Fill all voids and work out the air pockets by working the end of a rod in and out of the concrete.

Concrete Walls

The clean, smooth lines of a poured concrete wall adapt to any landscape or setting. Easily formed in curves, straight lines, or irregular shapes, walls of concrete are strong and durable with most applications requiring no more than 8" widths.

Concrete walls are widely used as foundations for many types of structures.

Concrete walls can also be used in garden or patio areas as decorative screens, borders, planter walls, tree wells, or retaining walls to control erosion or landscape an area.

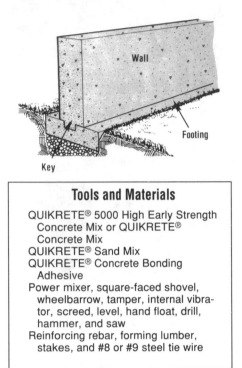

Wall

Footing

Key

BUILDING THE FORMS

The most important step in constructing a strong, attractive wall is building strong, accurate forms. Wall forms must be strong enough to withstand the great pressure exerted by the wet concrete; any failure in the forms will be disastrous. Keep in mind that building and aligning the forms for a poured concrete wall usually takes much longer than pouring and finishing the concrete.

A straight wall form is constructed of 1/2", 5/8", or 3/4" exterior grade plywood sheathing, studs, spacers, ties, and (for larger, heavier walls) wales. Sheathing forms the mold, while studs back up and support the sheathing. Spacers set and maintain spacing and support the form prior to the pour. Wire ties snug the form and resist the pressure of the wet concrete. Wales align the form and brace the studs in forms more than 4' to 5' high. Two horizontal wales are sufficient for most forms, but they should not be spaced greater than 30" on center.

For lower, lighter walls, it is possible to cast the wall at the same time you cast the footer. Larger walls always require separate pours for the footer and wall, with the wall keyed to the footer as shown in the illustration.

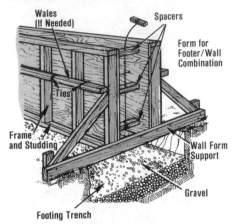

Wales (If Needed)   Spacers

Form for Footer/Wall Combination

Ties

Frame and Studding

Wall Form Support

Gravel

Footing Trench

To construct the forms:

1. Build the form in sections, using 2 × 4s laid on edge to construct frames that measure the height of the wall and no more than 8' in length. Nail 2 × 4 studs into each frame, spacing them on 16" centers.

2. Nail plywood sheathing to the frames. If needed, mark off the position of the wales and toenail them to the studs.

3. To install wire ties, drill 1/8" holes on either side of the wales or studs. Tilt two sections upright, face to face, spacing them at the desired wall thickness. Run a piece of wire through opposite holes in the form and around wales or studs. Twist the ends together to form a loop. Insert a properly sized spacer near the tie, and tighten down the tie by using a stick to twist the tie snug as shown. Remember to

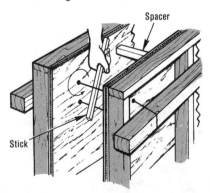

Spacer

Stick

attach pull wires around spacers so they can be removed as the pour is made.

4. Add on additional sections by nailing frames together through adjacent studding. The running length of the form should be slightly longer than the finished wall so that a stop board can be installed as shown.

5. Center the completed form over the footer, making certain it is plumb. Stake, brace, and nail the form firmly in place.

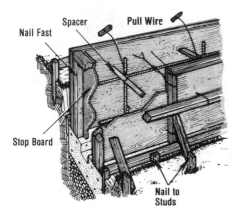

less than one hour between pours, lay a 1/2" to 1" layer of QUIKRETE® Sand Mix combined with QUIKRETE® Concrete Acrylic Fortifier on the previous pour to seal the joint prior to placing the next layer of concrete. This method *should not* be used if delays exceed one hour. Instead, coat the surface of the previous pour with QUIKRETE® Concrete Bonding Adhesive before pouring the next layer of concrete.

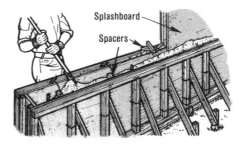

5. Strike off the concrete flush with the top of the form. Float and trowel it to the desired finish. Insert anchor bolts for mud sills and wooden caps once the concrete has set sufficiently to hold them.

POURING THE WALL

1. With the form properly mounted on the cured concrete footer, tie the wall rebar into the existing footer rebar. Coat the insides of the forms with clean oil or release agent.

2. Prepare the QUIKRETE® Concrete, QUIKRETE® 5000 or Fiber-Reinforced Concrete Mix to be used for the wall. Avoid using too much water and creating a soupy consistency—aggregates will settle toward the bottom and a weak wall will result.

3. Pour the wall in horizontal layers of not more than 20", beginning at the ends and moving toward the center. Use a ramp to wheel the concrete into position and a splashboard to direct the pour and control spillage. Remove the spacers as you go.

4. Work the concrete against the sides of the form and around the reinforcement as each layer is poured. Use an internal vibrator or strike the sides of the form with a hammer or mallet. Pour layers as soon after the previous one as possible to avoid cold (non-bonded) joints, which cause leaks. For delays of more than 20 minutes but

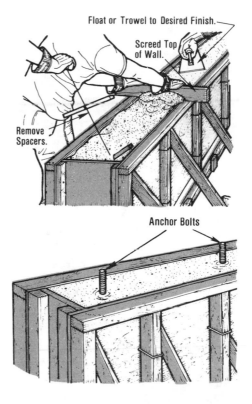

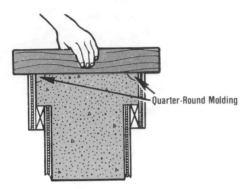

Quarter-Round Molding

6. Remove the forms after the concrete has cured for at least 3 to 4 days. The wire ties will eventually rust and stain the concrete if left in, so cut them out beneath the surface of the concrete. Patch the holes after wetting them down; apply QUIKRETE® Sand Mix or Vinyl Concrete Patcher flush with the surrounding surface.

7. Depending on the amount of concrete to be poured and the people available to do the job, it might be necessary to construct the wall in sections by using a movable stop board. Drill holes through the stop board so that it can be moved along the wall without cutting the rebar.

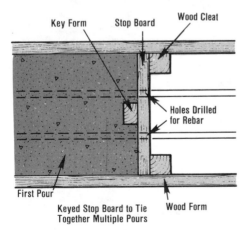

Key Form   Stop Board   Wood Cleat

Holes Drilled for Rebar

First Pour

Keyed Stop Board to Tie Together Multiple Pours   Wood Form

8. As each section is poured, allow it to set (12 to 24 hours) before removing the stop board. Before pouring the new section, coat the exposed end with QUIKRETE® Concrete Bonding Adhesive to avoid leaks caused by the cold joint.

For Best Results

Make curved forms by nailing multiple strips of saw-kerfed plywood or semi-flexible hardboard to the form studding.

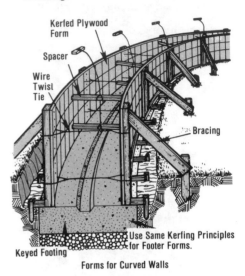

Kerfed Plywood Form

Spacer

Wire Twist Tie

Bracing

Use Same Kerfing Principles for Footer Forms.

Keyed Footing

Forms for Curved Walls

Concrete Retaining Walls

Retaining walls are used to prevent soil erosion of sharply sloping lawns. The principles of solid form construction must be used.

PLANNING THE WALL

Determine the height of the wall. To assure stability, the angle of a sloping lawn should never be greater than 45°, and the gentler the slope, the better. The higher the wall, the gentler the slope will be.

The dimensions of the retaining wall will vary according to the wall height, as shown in the table. The design shown here does not require steel reinforcement since the width of the base and the

Retaining Wall Construction Data

Exposed Wall Height (A)	Top Thickness (B)	Distance from Ground to Base (C)	Distance from Top to Base (D)	Base Depth (E)	Base Width (F)	Outside Base Extension (G)	Inside Base Extension (H)
12"	6"	4"	16"	6"	14"	3"	3"
18"	6"	6"	24"	6"	18"	3"	3"
24"	7"	8"	32"	8"	24"	4"	4"
30"	7"	10"	40"	10"	28"	4"	4"
36"	8"	12"	48"	12"	36"	6"	6"
42"	8"	14"	56"	12"	40"	6"	6"
48"	9"	16"	64"	12"	44"	6"	6"

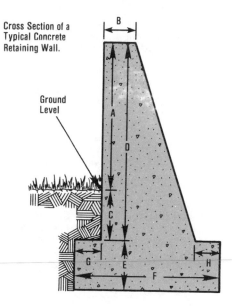

Cross Section of a Typical Concrete Retaining Wall.

above ground level. If the wall is higher than 4', place a second row of weep holes 3' above the first.

Details of the retaining wall form are shown here. As you can see, footer and wall are cast in one step. If the soil is sufficiently firm, use an earth form for the footer portion.

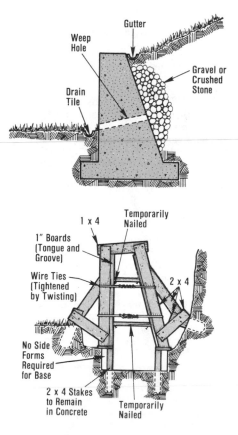

weight of the wall provide adequate support.

Good drainage is essential. Drainage is provided by filling coarse gravel behind the wall and by building weep holes into the wall. Make weep holes by inserting short lengths of 2" plastic pipe or 3" drain tile in the forms when they are built. The first row should be 2" to 4"

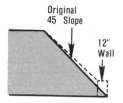

POURING THE WALL

Follow the mixing and pouring procedure recommended earlier. QUIKRETE® Concrete Mix or QUIKRETE® 5000 is recommended for heavier retaining walls. Because of the pressure created by the sloping aggregate, cure the concrete for at least 7 days before removing the forms. Once the forms are removed, tamp QUIKRETE® All-Purpose Gravel into the space behind the wall. Fill the top foot or so with topsoil, providing a gutter depression along the wall for better drainage.

Concrete Foundations

The three most common foundation designs are poured wall foundations, slab foundations, and pier or pillar foundations. The steps involved in constructing a poured wall foundation are illustrated on pages 13 through 16.

SLAB FOUNDATIONS

Slab foundations are simple and inexpensive, and they eliminate the need for major excavation, footings, and foundation walls. Three variations of slab foundation construction are used: desert, wet/warm area, and cold area. For any type of slab foundation, stake out the area with batter boards (see page 4) and remove the top layer of sod and soil. The tools and materials are similar to those used to pour typical concrete slabs (see page 5). The only exception is the rigid board insulation required for cold area construction.

QUIKRETE® Fiber-Reinforced Concrete Mix offers increased resistance to cracking and chipping for slab foundations that will also serve as concrete floors in garages, tool sheds, and other work buildings.

QUIKRETE® 5000 High Early Strength Concrete is designed for improved workability and rapid strength gains. It is ideal for a foundation project requiring extra strength and fast completion.

DESERT SLAB CONSTRUCTION

This type of foundation is constructed the same way as any slab, such as sidewalks or patios, except that a shallow

footing is poured with it This slab rests directly on the ground.

1. Remove the topsoil and dig the trench as shown.

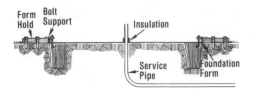

2. Install and insulate any service pipes needed for water, sewer, etc.
3. Construct the forms; stake and nail them firmly in position. Note how anchor bolts can be temporarily positioned for the placing of concrete.
4. Mix and place the concrete in the footer and slab forms in one continuous operation.

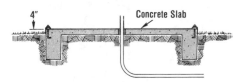

5. Screed, float, and trowel the concrete as if it were a sidewalk or patio (see page 7).
6. When constructing thicker slabs, use a 4″ base of QUIKRETE® All-Purpose Gravel or crushed stone to save on the amount of concrete used. For larger slabs use a length of 4″ x 4″ lumber as a temporary screed guide.

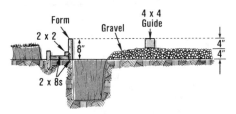

7. Cure the concrete for 3 to 4 days. For information on curing, refer to pages 2-3.

WET/WARM AREA CONSTRUCTION

This type of slab is used in wet/warm areas that are free of freezing problems. The footer and slab sections are poured in two steps, and a moisture barrier is installed.

1. Construct and install two separate forms as shown. Use short lengths of board to hold the inner form in position. Fill the inner form with an 8" base of QUIKRETE® All-Purpose Gravel or crushed stone and install a moisture barrier, such as 6-mil plastic sheathing, over the gravel.

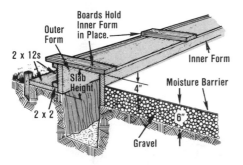

2. Place the concrete in the footer trench 4" short of the top of the form. Allow the concrete time to set up and retain its shape (1 to 2 days).

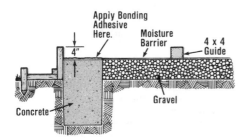

3. Remove the inner form. Apply a coat of QUIKRETE® Concrete Bonding Adhesive to the exposed footer surface.

4. Pour, screed, and finish the balance of the slab form, removing the temporary screed guides as you proceed.

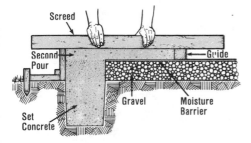

5. Cure the concrete for 3 to 4 days. For information on curing, refer to page 2.

COLD AREA CONSTRUCTION

The footer section of this slab must extend below the frost line, and the slab itself must be insulated with rigid board insulation.

1. Dig a 2'-wide footer trench to a depth several inches below the frost line. In firm soil, one side of the trench can act as a form. Construct and install the outer and inner form walls as shown.

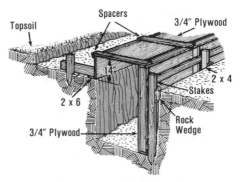

2. Pour the concrete to the top of the form, vibrate out air pockets, screed level, and install anchor bolts.

3. Remove the form and install 4" rigid insulation board on the inner side of the concrete foundation. Use soil to hold the insulation in place.

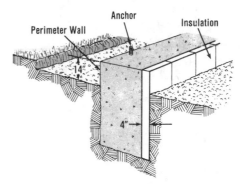

4. Lay down a 6" base of QUIKRETE® All-Purpose Gravel or crushed stone, cover with a moisture barrier, and lay rigid board insulation on top of the moisture barrier as shown.

5. Place a 4"-thick layer of concrete over the insulation board, screeding and finishing as before.

6. Cure the concrete for 3 to 4 days. For information on curing, refer to page 2.

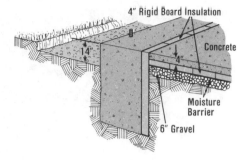

4" Rigid Board Insulation

14"

Concrete

4"

Moisture Barrier

6" Gravel

PIER AND PILLAR FOUNDATIONS

A pier foundation is simply an individual footer that supports a structural post or beam. Simple pier foundations are commonly used for small structures built with a crawl space design. Anchor bolts or plates are usually set in the pier footer before the concrete sets. This makes attaching the post or beam much simpler and results in the strongest possible application.

Pier foundations should be set deep enough in the ground to avoid shifting and upheaval caused by freeze/thaw cycles. A truncated pyramid shape saves on the amount of concrete used. Forms can be constructed of plywood or other sturdy lumber.

QUIK-TUBE™ Pillar Foundations

QUIK-TUBE™ rigid fiber building forms are the ideal method of pouring cylinder-shaped concrete foundations for deck and porch supports and other load-bearing applications. QUIK-TUBE™ forms can also be used to create attractive bases for lamp posts, fence posts, basketball net posts, mailbox posts, and other post-setting applications. Such

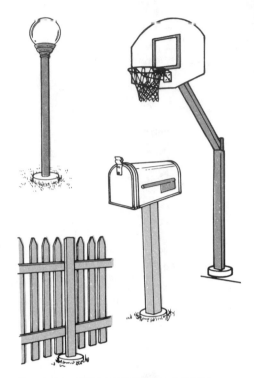

forms may also be required by frost line building codes.

QUIK-TUBE™ forms allow you to place the strongest foundation possible. The inner walls of the form are waxed. This holds in the concrete's water content, which results in maximum curing and strength buildup. Consider that when placed in a hole or dirt form, water can be sucked out of the concrete by the surrounding soil. This shortens curing time and reduces concrete strength. For this reason, many local building codes now specify the use of forms for all footers and foundations used in load-bearing applications.

QUIK-TUBE™ forms are available in 6", 8", 10", and 12" nominal diameters. Each tube is 4' long and can easily be cut to length using ordinary power tools. They

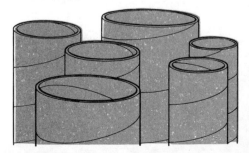

can be left in place or stripped away after the concrete has cured for 24 hours. For the easiest removal and the smoothest concrete finish, apply a release agent to the inside of the forms.

Pressure-treated wood or metal posts can be secured to the footer by anchor plates or bolts embedded in the concrete. The posts themselves can also be embedded in the concrete to a depth that ensures complete support. The exact method acceptable for load-bearing applications such as decks are subject to local building codes.

For example, in areas prone to termite problems, the code may specify the use of pressure-treated lumber attached to the footer using anchor plates. The elevation of the footer may be several inches above grade. These steps keep the lumber from direct contact with the soil, a condition that reduces the likelihood of termite problems.

Flag, basketball, and playground equipment poles may require embedding in concrete to certain depths, often up to 1/3 overall pole height. Check local codes and/or pole manufacturer recommendations.

Tools and Materials

QUIK-TUBE™ Building Forms
QUIKRETE® Fast-Setting Concrete or
  QUIKRETE® Concrete Mix
QUIKRETE® All-Purpose Gravel or
  crushed stone
Shovel or posthole digger, tamper,
  hammer, and mason's level
Lumber for braces and nails
Wood preservative and/or rust
  inhibitor
Paintbrush
Concrete release agent (if required)
Anchoring hardware (if required)

POSITIONING THE FORM

1. The diameter of the QUIK-TUBE™ form should be at least double the post or pillar diameter it will support. When supporting deck posts or other load-bearing members the form should extend down below the frost line.

2. Use a posthole digger or shovel to dig a hole to the proper depth. Do not make the hole wider than needed to minimize backfilling.

3. Place 6" of QUIKRETE® All-Purpose Gravel on the base of the hole to help with drainage.

4. Cut the QUIK-TUBE™ rigid form to size. In most cases you will want to size the form so that the finished footing will extend out of the ground approximately 2" to 6". This protects lumber from direct contact with the ground and allows rainwater to drain rapidly from the area.

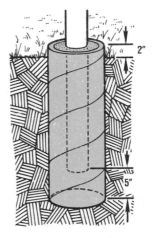

5. Center the form in the hole. Check that the top of the form is level using a mason's level.

6. Carefully backfill against the sides of the QUIK-TUBE™ form to support the tube and keep it from shifting during the pour.

7. When forms are placed aboveground in applications that will be backfilled later, make sure the bottom of the QUIK-TUBE™ is properly braced. Build a bottom collar out of scrap lumber, and keep the form plumb by adding braces above its midpoint as needed. Nail and stake all braces firmly in place.

POSITIONING THE POST

When the post or pillar is to be embedded in the concrete, position it inside the QUIK-TUBE™ prior to beginning the pour. Use pressure-treated lumber or apply creosote equivalent to prevent below-the-ground rot. Coat metal posts with rust inhibitor. Center the post or pillar inside the form. Brace it as needed to prevent shifting during the pour and while the concrete sets. Use a mason's level to make certain the post is plumb and its top is level.

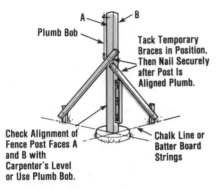

A   B
Plumb Bob

Tack Temporary Braces in Position. Then Nail Securely after Post Is Aligned Plumb.

Check Alignment of Fence Post Faces A and B with Carpenter's Level or Use Plumb Bob.

Chalk Line or Batter Board Strings

ESTIMATING CONCRETE NEEDS

For a cylindrical form, such as QUIK-TUBE™, multiply the square of the forms radius (one-half its diameter) by 3.1416. This gives you the area of the QUIK-TUBE™ form. Multiply this area by the form height to determine the volume of concrete needed.

For example, for an 8″ diameter form measuring 4′ in length, the calculation would be:

$$8″ \div 2 = 4″ \text{ or } .33 \text{ ft radius}$$
$$.33 \text{ ft}^2 \times 3.1416 = .342 \text{ ft}^2$$
$$.342 \text{ ft}^2 \times 4 \text{ ft} = 1.36 \text{ ft}^3 \text{ of concrete}$$

The table given below simplifies the calculation process for QUIK-TUBE™ jobs. It lists the bags of mix needed per linear foot of QUIK-TUBE™ form for the various tube diameters. For example, if you are using 50-pound bags of QUIK-

RETE® Fast-Setting Concrete, to pour the 8″ diameter, 4′ long form the calculation would be:

1 bag per linear foot x 4′ = 4 bags

If 80-pound bags of QUIKRETE® Concrete mix were used, the calculation would be:

3/5 bag per linear foot x 4′ = 2-2/5 bags

PLACING THE CONCRETE

QUIKRETE® Fast-Setting Concrete is the ideal concrete mix for this job. It gains its initial set in 20-40 minutes and reaches a strength of 1000 psi in 1 day so construction work can continue almost uninterrupted. QUIKRETE® Concrete Mix is another excellent mix for constructing QUIK-TUBE™ footers.

1. Apply concrete release agent if the smoothest possible concrete surface is desired.

2. Mix and place the concrete in the form. Work it down and around any post or pillar set in the form, but do not use a mechanical vibrator to settle the concrete.

3. Carefully embed any anchor plates or bolts needed in the top of the form. Make absolutely certain these anchors are centered and level before the concrete gains its initial set.

4. If forms are to be removed, do so within 24 hours. Cut the QUIK-TUBE™ with a sharp knife or power saw set to the correct cutting depth. Simply peel the form away from the concrete.

For Best Results

Store QUIK-TUBE™ forms at least 4″ off the ground. Cover them to keep dry. Never place concrete into a wet QUIK-TUBE™ form.

Never use a mechanical vibrator to compact concrete inside a QUIK-TUBE™ form.

Never reuse a QUIK-TUBE™ form.

Bags of Concrete Needed Per Foot of Form Height				
QUIK-TUBE™ Diameter	6″	8″	10″	12″
QUIKRETE® Fast-Setting Concrete 50-lb bags	1/2	1	1-2/5	2
QUIKRETE® Concrete Mix 80-lb bags	1/3	3/5	1	1-1/3
QUIKRETE® Concrete Mix 60-lb bags	1/2	4/5	1-1/4	1-3/4
QUIKRETE® Fiber-Reinforced Concrete Mix 60-lb bags	1-1/2	4/5	1-1/4	1-3/4

Wood Decks

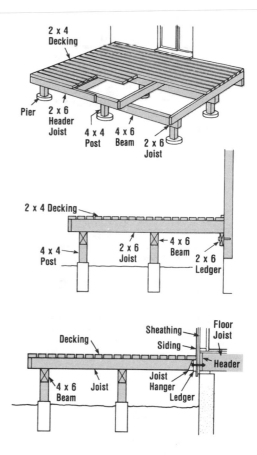

When planning your wood deck, take time to consider what you really want the project to accomplish. Consider your lifestyle and family preferences for fun in the sun, relaxed lounging in cooling shade, the need for privacy, and the scope of activities you want your deck to accommodate.

You should also note the prevailing wind patterns, the direction and angle of morning and afternoon sun, plus the view from the deck. Plantings and screen walls can provide more privacy, screen out undesirable views, and buffer winter winds. You can also position the deck to take advantage of existing shade trees or sunny exposures.

A deck is one project that absolutely requires checking into local building code requirements. Codes may specify setback distances from property lines, restrictions on deck height, and certain construction details, such as how to attach the deck to existing structures, or stair and railing details.

LUMBER FOR DECKS

Lumber for outdoor projects should be highly resistant to moisture and insects. Pressure-treated lumber is a good economic choice. Preservatives forced deep into the wood fibers give this lumber its distinctive green or yellow tint. The color will fade to a silver-gray when exposed to weather. Pressure-treated lumber can also be stained. Redwood and cedar are woods naturally resistant to insects and decay. While available in some sections of the country, they may be cost prohibitive for larger projects.

The four main components of the deck are the posts, beams, joists, and decking. Posts consist of 4 × 4 lumber. Beams typically measure 4 × 6, and are usually made by nailing two 2 × 6 pieces back to back. Joists are normally 2 × 6 lumber. Face decking boards are either 2 × 2, 2 × 4, or 2 × 6. Decking boards can be layed flat or positioned on edge.

Posts support the beams, which in turn support the joists. Deck facing is attached to the joists. Maximum spans for beam and joist pieces are given in the tables to follow. These are conservative estimates designed to help you plan your deck and estimate materials. The exact strength of the lumber depends on the species used. The method of connection may also affect final loading strength. Always check beam and joist span and spacing specifications against local building codes. Your lumber dealer may also help you select the best lumber choices from the species and sizes available in your area.

Beam Span	
Beam Size	Max. Span Allowed when Laid on Edge
4×4 or two 2×4s	4 ft
4×6 or two 2×6s	6 ft
4×8 or two 2×8s	8 ft
4×10 or two 2×10s	10 ft
4×12 or two 6×10s	12 ft
6×10 or two 2×10s	12 ft
6×12 or two 2×12s	14 ft

Joist Span	
Joist	Max. Span Allowed when Laid on Edge
2×6 (min.)	@ 12 in. o.c. 8 ft
	@ 16 in. o.c. 7 ft
	@ 24 in. o.c. 5 ft
2×8	@ 12 in. o.c. 10 ft
	@ 16 in. o.c. 9 ft
	@ 24 in. o.c. 7 ft
2×10	@ 12 in. o.c. 13 ft
	@ 16 in. o.c. 12 ft
	@ 24 in. o.c. 10 ft
2×12	@ 12 in. o.c. 16 ft
	@ 16 in. o.c. 15 ft
	@ 24 in. o.c. 14 ft

NOTE: O.C. stands for on center (of joist).

FASTENERS FOR DECKS

Wood members can be joined together using nails, screws, bolts, or lag screws. Metal nailing straps, joist hangers, post anchors, and other special hardware pieces make joining members easier and more accurate. All fasteners and hardware must be galvanized or otherwise non-rusting to prevent staining of the wood.

Always nail through thinner members into thicker stock. Nails should penetrate the thicker back piece by twice the thickness of the thinner piece, but no more than 1-1/2". Screws should penetrate the receiving member by at least the thickness of the thinner member, but never less than 1". Carriage bolts require washers under their nuts, while machine bolts and lag screws need flat washers at both their head and nut ends to keep from crushing the wood when tightened. Lag screws should be installed with a washer. Pilot holes for bolts should be the same diameter as the bolt shank. Pilot holes for screws and lag screws should be the diameter of the solid portion of the screw between the threads.

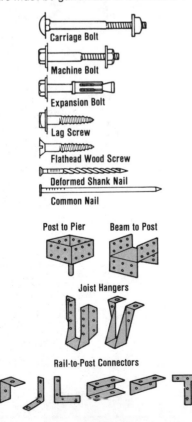

Carriage Bolt

Machine Bolt

Expansion Bolt

Lag Screw

Flathead Wood Screw

Deformed Shank Nail

Common Nail

Post to Pier   Beam to Post

Joist Hangers

Rail-to-Post Connectors

POST PLACEMENT

1. Lay out string lines and construct batter boards to locate the position of corner and intermediate posts. Use the layout methods covered on pages 4 to 5.

2. Dig postholes and place concrete post footings using QUIK-TUBE™ Building Forms. (See page 20 for details.) Consult local building codes for the accepted method of setting posts in your area. The method most often specified uses a post anchor embedded in the concrete footer. Be sure this anchor is positioned properly. After the concrete has gained its final set (at least 24 hours) attach the post to the anchor. If you plan to embed the post in the wet concrete of the footer, be sure it is properly centered and set deep enough to provide proper support.

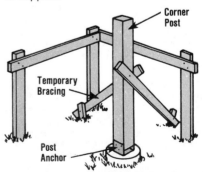

Corner Post

Temporary Bracing

Post Anchor

3. Do not cut the posts to finished height at this time. The exact height of the posts will depend on the method used to set and secure the joists to the beams.

LEDGERS

Decks that attach to an existing house require the use of a ledger. A ledger is a 2 × 6 or 2 × 8 piece of lumber that attaches to the house with bolts, which extend through the ledger, house siding, house sheathing, and box header of the house frame. It is also possible to attach the ledger to concrete or masonry surfaces using expansion type anchors and lag bolts.

When joist hangers are used, the tops of the joists are level with the top of the ledger. The proper position for the ledger is 1" down from any existing door sill, plus the thickness of the decking face. The ledger must also extend 2" beyond the last joist position to allow room for securing the metal joist hanger.

When hangers are not used, the joists rest on top of the ledger and are toe-nailed or otherwise fastened to it. In this case, the proper ledger position is 1" down from existing door sills, plus the thickness of the decking face, plus the height of the joist.

In either case, the ledger should also be flashed with metal to prevent water from seeping between the ledger and house. Check all measurements before fastening the ledger, and be sure to use the actual, not the nominal dimensions of the lumber when calculating the overall thickness of the joists and deck facing.

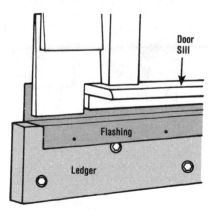

Be sure you understand the exact position and elevation of the ledger, joists, beams, and posts before attaching the ledger or cutting off the posts to their required heights. The method you select for attaching joists to the ledger and beams will affect the height of the posts. It is helpful to study the illustrations given here in understanding the relationship of deck components.

BEAMS

The 4 × 6 beams that support the joists normally rest on top of the posts. However, you may also plan to run the posts up through the deck to serve as supports for a railing. If this is the case, sandwich the posts between the two 2 × 6 pieces of stock that make up the beam and secure using bolts and washers or nailed wooden cleats.

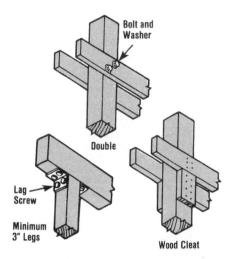

To determine the proper cutoff or attachment height for the posts:

1. Attach a line level to the ledger at the point where the bottom of the joist will be located.

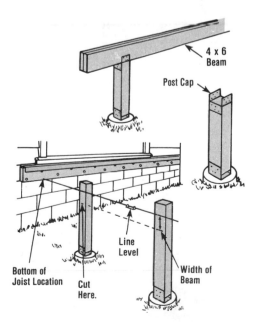

2. Run the line level out to the posts in that row, and carefully mark this elevation on the posts.

3. Measure down from this point a distance equal to the thickness of the beam. (For a 6″ nominal beam, this is usually 5-1/2″.)

4. If the posts will not serve as rail supports, cut them off at this level. Cut carefully to ensure the tops of the posts are level. Secure the beams to the post using post cap anchors or angle irons. If the posts will serve as railing supports, the position marked in step 3 is where the bottom edge of the beam pieces will be located as they are sandwiched around and bolted to the posts.

JOISTS

1. Attach the joists to beams by resting the joists directly on top of the beams and attaching them with fasteners called framing anchors or beam saddles.

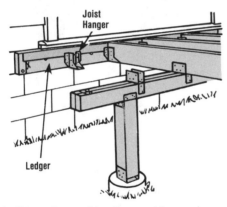

2. If two pieces of lumber must be used to create a long joist run, be sure the joint is located over a beam location.

3. Nail solid 2 x 6 bridging pieces (intermediate joists) between the main joists when spanning long distances. This bridging will keep the main joists from twisting and help distribute the load on the deck.

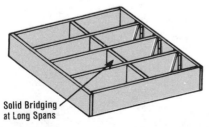

Solid Bridging at Long Spans

4. Attach a 2 × 6 header joist to the front of the deck to cover the ends of the joists. This header joist acts as a facing and nailer for intermediate railing supports.

DECKING

Decking is most often made of 2-by material, such as 2 × 2, 2 × 4, or 2 × 6 lumber. Exterior grade plywood or sheathing is also used as deck facing if outdoor carpeting is being installed. The simplest method of laying 2-by decking is to run boards all in one direction. More intricate patterns can be created if adequate joist supports are installed.

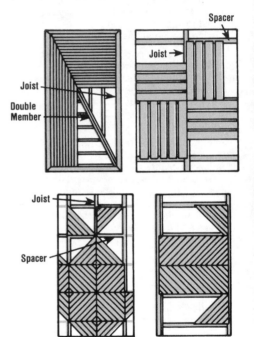

1. Check the end grain of each board before nailing. Position the board so its end rings curve up. In other words, the bark side of the lumber is facing up. This helps eliminate cupping.

2. Lay the first deck board perfectly square since it will serve as a guide for the remaining boards. Drive two nails into each decking board at each joist.

3. All deck board joints must occur above a joist. Stagger adjacent board joints to eliminate a continuous deck board joint. Maintain proper spacing between boards using a 1/4″ spacer strip.

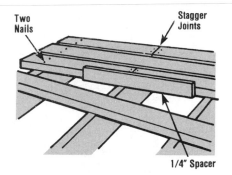

Two Nails

Stagger Joints

1/4" Spacer

4. Periodically measure the distance remaining to be covered with decking. Take measurements at both ends and the midpoint and keep the boards running parallel to one another. Make any corrections gradually over a span of several boards.

5. When there is roughly 6' of decking remaining to be layed, begin adjusting the spacing between boards so the deck will end with a full board.

TRIMMING DECKING

Allow the deck boards to slightly overlap the edges of the deck. Do not attempt to cut each piece to size as you nail it. After all the decking boards are fastened, snap a chalk line at the desired edge of the deck. You can then cut all boards to size using a power saw. Tacking a wooden guide strip for the saw to ride against is the best method of ensuring a straight, even cut along the chalk line.

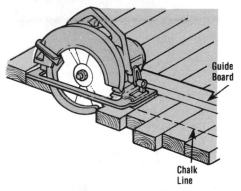

Guide Board

Chalk Line

FREESTANDING DECKS

If you do not plan to access the deck through a door to your home, a freestanding deck design may be your ideal choice. A freestanding deck eliminates the problems associated with attaching the deck to your home's frame or foundation. A freestanding deck can be built ad-

jacent to your home, or in a shady corner of your property away from the house.

The freestanding deck uses the same post, beam, joist, and decking system used for an attached deck. Joists can be set on top of beams or hung between beams using joist hangers. Once again, it is important to establish the final height of your deck and cut posts to the proper elevation.

STAIRS

The stringers, or side supports for the stair treads, are the most important part of the stair design. They must be accurately marked and cut to ensure success. The most common stair design used for decks is the open riser/open stringer type.

1. Measure the height of the deck to the ground (total rise) and the distance from the deck to the base of the stairs (total run).

2. Most stairs have a rise of about 7" and a run of about 10" to 11". Divide these figures into the rise and run to see if the distances can be covered with an equal number of steps. Make slight adjustments to the rise and run as needed, but never vary the rise and run between steps. Include the thickness of the thread material in your rise calculations. Two-by lumber is actually 1-5/8" thick.

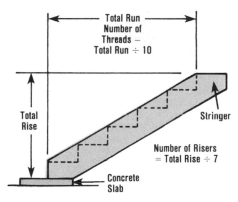

Total Run
Number of Threads —
Total Run ÷ 10

Total Rise

Stringer

Number of Risers = Total Rise ÷ 7

Concrete Slab

3. When the exact location of the stair base is determined, pour a small slab foundation so the base of the stairs will be level and perfectly supported. Use QUIKRETE® Concrete Mix or QUIKRETE® Fast-Setting Concrete Mix. Slab thickness should be 4˝ minimum. Refer to page 5 for the procedures used to mix, place and finish a simple concrete slab. Install anchors

at the proper locations so the stringers can be firmly fastened to the slab.

4. Stringers are made using 2 × 10 or 2 × 12 lumber. Mark off the rise height on one leg of a framing square and the depth of the thread on the other leg.

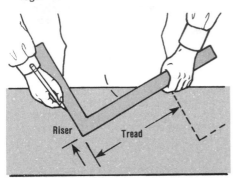

5. Cut the stringer out using a hand or power saw. Check that the stringer is properly sized, and then use it as a template to create the other stringer.

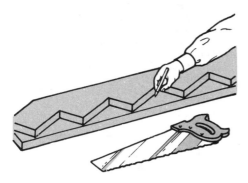

6. To keep the rise equal on all steps, cut a strip of lumber off the bottom riser that is equal in thickness to the tread thickness.

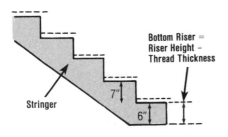

7. Attach the top of the stringer to the deck joists using hangers or lag bolts. Secure the bottom of the steps to the concrete slab anchors.

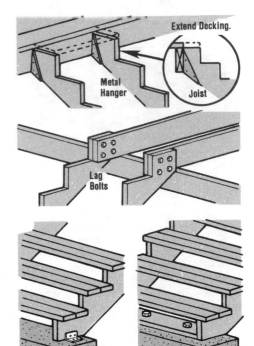

8. Nail the tread boards in place, bark side up. They can be trimmed flush to the stringers or allowed to overlap.

RAILINGS

Railings are needed to ensure personal safety on all but true ground level decks. Building codes often list deck railing specifications, so check with local authorities before finalizing your design. In general, the vertical and horizontal railing members must be spaced close enough to keep children from slipping through. Screening can also be used to close off openings between posts and rails.

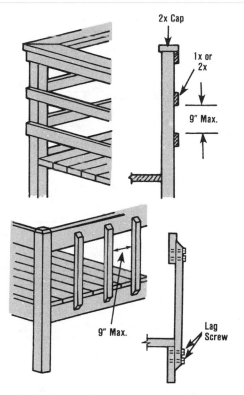

2x Cap

1x or 2x

9" Max.

9" Max.

Lag Screw

Railing posts that are not actual deck support posts must be secured to the joists, ledger, or beams using lag screws or carriage bolts. Never use nails to attach railing posts and never fasten them to the deck surface boards.

For Best Results

Low decks will shade the lawn beneath, and the lawn will die out. Remove the sod now and use it on bare spots elsewhere on your lawn. To prevent weeds from growing under the deck, cover the bare soil with heavy black plastic film topped with crushed stone, QUIKRETE® Marble Chips or Deco Pebbles, or bark chips.

Use and maintain an effective sealer on all pressure-treated lumber projects.

Dispose of all scraps of pressure-treated lumber in ordinary trash. Do not burn.

Reduce splitting of boards when nailed by blunting the nail point or predrilling pilot holes that are 3/4 the nail shank diameter.

In softer woods, use a larger washer under the carriage bolt heads.

Concrete Driveways and Curbs

Concrete driveways are constructed in the same manner as slabs, with certain key differences in design. Driveways for single-car garages are normally 10' to 14' wide; they must be at least 14' wide if the driveway curves. For two-car garages, the driveway is usually about 24' wide. A single-lane driveway that serves a two-car garage should begin to widen 15' to 20' before reaching the garage doors. Driveways can be built with turnaround areas in order to avoid backing vehicles out into traffic.

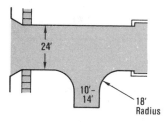

24'

10'-14'

18' Radius

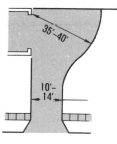

35'-40'

10'-14'

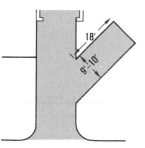

18'

9"-10'

An alternative to the basic slab driveway is the strip driveway. It has one strip of concrete under each wheel, approximately 3' to 4' wide and 5' center to center, with space between the strips. One caution with this type of driveway, however, is that it shifts more easily with changes in ground conditions than the slab type. It therefore requires some type of reinforcement, preferably iron or steel rebar.

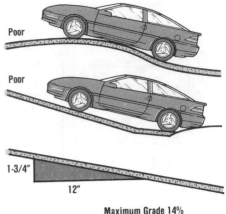

Poor

Poor

1-3/4"

12"

**Maximum Grade 14%
or 1-3/4" per Foot**

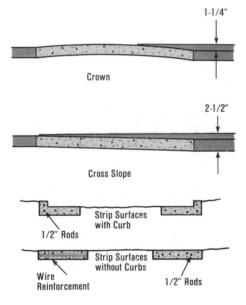

1-1/4"

Crown

2-1/2"

Cross Slope

Strip Surfaces
with Curb

1/2" Rods

Strip Surfaces
without Curbs

Wire
Reinforcement   1/2" Rods

Driveway thickness depends solely on the weight of the vehicles that will be using it. If it will serve only passenger cars, 4" is sufficient. If, on the other hand, trucks and other heavy vehicles will be using the driveway, a thickness of 5" or 6" is recommended.

DRIVEWAY GRADE

Driveway grade must be carefully planned if the garage is located above or below street level. A 14% grade (1-3/4" vertical rise for each running foot) is the recommended maximum, and it should be done gradually to avoid scraping the bumper or underside of the vehicles. For drainage purposes, a driveway should always be sloped slightly toward the street; 1/4" per running foot is sufficient. A crown or cross slope can be used for this purpose.

When constructing a driveway after the street, curbs, and public walks are in place, consult your local building codes; the part of the driveway between the

street and the sidewalk is usually controlled by the local municipality. Permission must usually be obtained before you can cut away part of the curb to accommodate a driveway entrance. If the driveway is built before the public walk, it must meet the proposed sidewalk grade and then drop to meet the top of the curb or gutter.

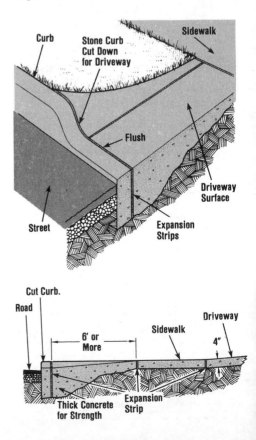

Curb   Stone Curb
        Cut Down
        for Driveway   Sidewalk

Flush

Street

Driveway
Surface

Expansion
Strips

Cut Curb.
Road   Driveway

                        Sidewalk   4"

6' or
More

Thick Concrete   Expansion
for Strength   Strip

ADDING A CURB

When adding a curb to the end of a driveway, drill two 1/2"-diameter holes into the driveway. These holes should be 3" deep and approximately 2' apart. Insert a 6" steel reinforcing rod in each hole. To construct the forms, stake a 2 × 8 flat against the edge of the driveway; the inside forms cannot be staked, so nail two short 2 × 4s perpendicular to the form, extending in toward the center of the driveway. Use bricks to weigh down the 2 × 4 supports. After pouring the concrete, round the inside edge of the curb with a trowel. This curb will be 6" wide and extend 4" above the driveway.

Concrete Patios

A patio is most often placed adjacent to a rear or side door, but it can also be freestanding or connected to the home by a separate walkway. In its most simple form, a patio is no more than a strategically placed concrete slab. But with a little imagination, it offers a great opportunity for combining unique design and surface treatments with the practicality of concrete construction. Don't feel limited to plain square or rectangular designs; curved and other free-form patios are visually striking additions to a home's exterior.

LOCATION

An important design consideration is to place the patio in relation to the sun. Take the time to examine the proposed site, noting the position and intensity of the sun during different times of the day. Also keep in mind factors such as the direction from which the prevailing winds blow, whether the area lends itself to landscaping with protective trees or screen walls, and the view. The following briefly summarizes the various exposures to help in the placement of a patio.

East. A patio facing east will cool down after high noon because it is shaded by the house. An eastern exposure is ideal for hot summer climates, but some form of side screening might be needed to combat the chill of fall.

West. A patio facing west provides plenty of sun year-round. However, excessive summer heat can be a problem in the late afternoon and evening—precisely when the patio is used most. Well-placed trees and shrubs not only provide cooling relief, but also add to the patio's natural setting.

North. Unless the patio is enclosed, a northern exposure is the least desirable setup. The patio receives minimal sunshine, thus keeping it cool and damp in all seasons but summer.

South. A patio facing south receives varying degrees of sunlight throughout the year. While southern exposures can get very warm during the height of summer, glare from the setting sun isn't the problem it is with a western exposure.

DESIGN FACTORS

The distance from the top of a finished patio surface to the doorway of the house should be no more than 8". If your patio will be more than 8" below the doorway, build it up with a thicker crushed stone subgrade. Another option is to build a wide concrete step on the patio, adjacent to the doorway.

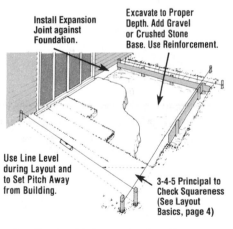

Install Expansion Joint against Foundation.

Excavate to Proper Depth. Add Gravel or Crushed Stone Base. Use Reinforcement.

Use Line Level during Layout and to Set Pitch Away from Building.

3-4-5 Principal to Check Squareness (See Layout Basics, page 4)

A patio should slope away from the house at the rate of 1/8" per running foot. Generally, a 4"-thick slab set 2" above ground level is suitable. To ensure that the height and slope are correct, begin the excavation, layout, and form construction where the patio meets the house.

Openings in the patio for tree wells, flower beds, and the like can be made by building forms of the proper size and leveling them with the perimeter forms. (Refer to pages 8 and 14 to 16 for more on form construction.) Stake the forms on the inside and cut the stakes flush with the top edge for easy screeding. When the concrete is poured, the forms will act as a dam to keep the concrete from flowing into the opening.

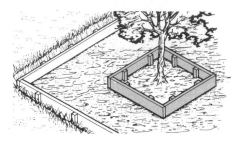

CONSTRUCTION

An attractive and durable patio can be made by combining wooden strips with concrete slab construction methods. Redwood is an excellent choice because of its high resistance to rot and decay. Tools and Materials are the same as those for concrete slabs (see page 5).

1. Construct the exterior form. Use the same type of wood that you will use for the strips because the exterior form is not removed after the concrete is placed.

2. Divide the area into boxes, using 2 × 4 lengths of the wood. Notch each piece at the intersections. The patio dimensions should be in multiples of the desired box sizes.

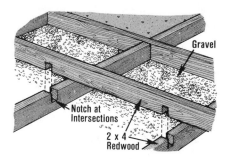

3. Place the cross members on edge and nail them securely into the exterior form frame.

4. Apply a wood sealer/stain before placing the concrete.

5. Mix and place the concrete as described in the section on concrete slabs, pages 5-7. Take care in placing the concrete to avoid having bits of it dry over the strips.

6. When the concrete begins to set, scrub the wood surfaces thoroughly.

FREE-FORM DESIGNS

Free-form or irregularly shaped patios can be circular, oval, or most any shape imaginable. The formwork is made of thin plywood or kerfed 1"-thick lumber. The major drawback with free-form designs is that the amount of usable patio space is reduced. For example, a square patio measuring 20' on a side provides 400 square feet of surface area, while a circular patio with a diameter of 20' provides only about 315 square feet of surface area.

The best way to estimate how much concrete will be needed is to draw a proportional outline of the patio. Do the drawing on a piece of graph paper, with each square representing 1 square foot. Just add up the number of full, 3/4, 1/2, and 1/4 squares to get the total area to be covered. The placement of the concrete is similar to a large driveway job.

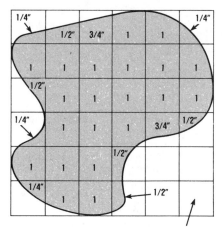

Graph Squares

Special Concrete Finishes

There are many alternatives to the standard smooth concrete finish; to select the right one, it is important to make a few practical considerations. For example, will the surface require frequent and thorough cleaning? If so, you should probably stick with a smooth finish, which is much easier to maintain than finishes that are grooved or heavily broomed. Also, will the surface be subjected to freeze/thaw conditions, abrasion, or heavy traffic? If so, avoid splattered finishes, which are more likely to peel and spall. And, if the surface will be subjected to traffic, is good traction a requirement? If so, plan to apply a floated, rough aggregate or an evenly grooved finish because they provide the best footing. Once all the practical considerations have been made, you can make your final decision based on such factors as visual appeal, color scheme, and location. Keep in mind that you can use a combination of finishes in a single project.

When a coarse finish is desired for non-slip footing, floating, edging, and grooving may be the only steps performed. When a denser, smoother finish is required, the surface is troweled once or several times with a stainless steel trowel. Troweling takes place after the surface moisture has evaporated from the surface and the concrete has lost its sheen. This setting time may vary greatly with weather conditions and the moisture content of the mix, from 30 minutes to several hours. Thirty minutes to an hour is average in most cases.

ROUGH-FLOATED FINISH

Rough concrete provides good traction, so it is particularly suited for pool decks and other areas frequently exposed to water. It is also more durable than smooth concrete. Work the concrete with a wooden hand float; if the surface is very large, use a darby or bull float. Move the float in various patterns until the desired effect is achieved.

SMOOTH FINISH

A smooth finish is practical, easy to clean, and ideal for making decorative inscriptions and impressions. Use a steel trowel, moving it in sweeping arcs; overlap the arcs to make sure the entire slab is smooth.

For very smooth surfaces, additional trowelings are necessary. On the second troweling, hold the leading edge up slightly and press down a bit harder. Repeat the process used in the first troweling. The third troweling should produce an almost glossy finish. Hold the leading edge up further, press down harder, and repeat the troweling process.

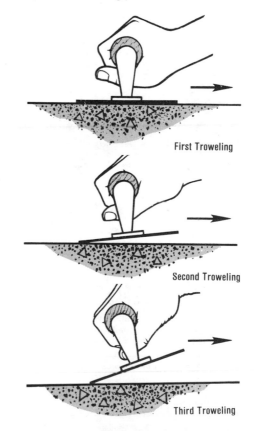

First Troweling

Second Troweling

Third Troweling

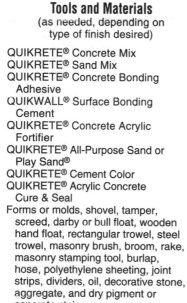

Tools and Materials
(as needed, depending on
type of finish desired)

QUIKRETE® Concrete Mix
QUIKRETE® Sand Mix
QUIKRETE® Concrete Bonding
  Adhesive
QUIKWALL® Surface Bonding
  Cement
QUIKRETE® Concrete Acrylic
  Fortifier
QUIKRETE® All-Purpose Sand or
  Play Sand®
QUIKRETE® Cement Color
QUIKRETE® Acrylic Concrete
  Cure & Seal
Forms or molds, shovel, tamper,
  screed, darby or bull float, wooden
  hand float, rectangular trowel, steel
  trowel, masonry brush, broom, rake,
  masonry stamping tool, burlap,
  hose, polyethylene sheeting, joint
  strips, dividers, oil, decorative stone,
  aggregate, and dry pigment or
  concrete stain

BROOMED FINISHES

Brooming can achieve a wide range of effects, depending on how soon you apply the broom, whether the bristles are soft or hard, and whether you use it wet or dry. Simply pull the broom across the concrete while it is still soft. Be sure to rinse the bristles frequently to keep the tips clean.

A damp, stiff-bristled broom produces a coarse texture, which is ideal for slopes and heavy traffic areas. Medium to fine textures are created with a dry, soft-bristled broom. Always pull the broom toward you in parallel, slightly overlapping strokes; never push it back and forth. Sidewalks and driveways should be broomed at right angles to the direction of traffic. Use the broom to create curves, waves, even herringbone patterns.

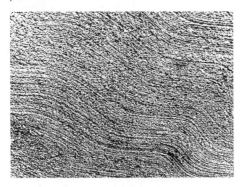

GROOVED AND STAMPED FINISHES

Grooved and stamped finishes are produced by pressing masonry stamping tools and other objects into slightly stiff concrete. Stamping tools available at most large rental centers can be used to imprint simulated paving brick, stone, tile, and other patterns. Small coarse aggregate such as pea gravel should be placed in the concrete prior to the stamp-

ing. After the surface has been floated and troweled, simply step on the pad to stamp the design to a depth of about 1".

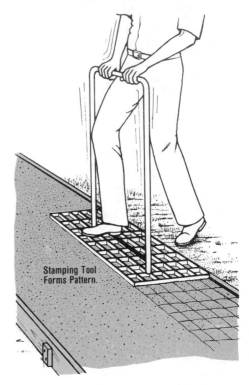

Stamping Tool Forms Pattern.

A piece of bent pipe works particularly well for making deep, clean grooves, and a jointer can be used to groove the concrete to look like flagstone. Scoring must be done when the concrete has partially set. For a unique finish, create your own homemade stamp using typical household items such as cookie cutters.

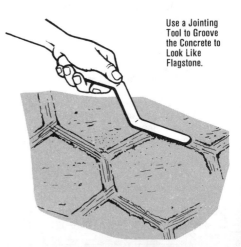

Use a Jointing Tool to Groove the Concrete to Look Like Flagstone.

SPLATTERED FINISH

Splattered finishes are undeniably beautiful and unusual, but they are also less durable than other finishes and are most often used on walks.

They are not recommended in cold climates because of the likelihood of standing water in the depressions freezing and cracking the finish. The most common splattered finish is the travertine effect; this is achieved by first applying QUIKRETE® Concrete Bonding Adhesive to the concrete. When it becomes tacky, splatter a 1/2" layer of QUIKRETE® Sand Mix onto the surface with a large brush and trowel very lightly over the high spots.

A similar effect can be achieved by pressing QUIKRETE® Rock Salt into the surface of freshly floated or troweled concrete. Leave the tops of the salt grains exposed so that they can be removed by washing and light scrubbing after the concrete has cured. The result is a randomly pitted surface.

RUBBED AND HAMMERED AGGREGATE FINISHES

A powdery, dusty effect can be produced by applying a thin layer of QUIKRETE® All-Purpose Sand or Play Sand® onto a concrete surface that has partially set. Shake the sand over the entire surface, then rub it in using a piece of clean burlap.

Medium-sized aggregate (including pebbles, small gravel, and seashell fragments) can be hammered into fresh concrete. Use a screed to evenly distribute the force of each blow.

EXPOSED-STONE AND COARSE-AGGREGATE FINISHES

Stones of various shapes and sizes can be individually hand-set or sown like seeds onto a surface of slightly stiff concrete. Coarse aggregate, such as large gravel, may be applied in the same way. Be sure to use clean, damp stones; after the application, press them into the mix (or slightly under the surface) with a heavy screed. Next, use a stiff-bristled broom to remove any excess mortar. Finally, clean the surface with a fine spray of water until there is no noticeable cement film left on the aggregate.

Larger cobblestone and river stone can also be set in the surface of concrete

slabs and step treads. This technique is very similar to setting pavers in a mortar bed. The fresh concrete must not be allowed to set up too stiffly before placing the stone. Press the stones into the concrete so that more than half of each one is embedded. Cover the stones with a piece of wood to protect them from being damaged if you find it necessary to hammer them into place. Brush between stones with a small hand broom for clean, even joints.

COLORED FINISHES

One method of coloring concrete is to pre-mix QUIKRETE® liquid Cement Color with water before adding it to the dry concrete mix. This method ensures uniform color within a single batch. When coloring concrete in several batches, the proportions must be carefully controlled to achieve uniform results.

A second coloring method involves spreading dry coloring material over the concrete after it has been leveled and floated. Apply about two-thirds of the total amount of coloring material in a first application, finish as you would normally, then repeat the procedure with the remaining material.

A third coloring method has the paint, colored coating, or pigmented stain applied to the concrete after it has cured. The easiest way to apply paint to concrete or masonry is with a long nap (3/4" to 1") roller. As for staining, the concrete or mortar must be at least 60 days old prior to the application. Stains can be applied with a brush, roller, or airless sprayer.

CURING & SEALING

No matter what type of concrete finish is chosen, for best results use QUIKRETE® Acrylic Concrete Cure & Seal as the final step in achieving a durable and sealed concrete surface.

Concrete Steps and Ramps

Steps constructed from QUIKRETE® Concrete Mix or QUIKRETE® 5000 High

Early Strength Concrete Mix are attractive and durable, and can provide good traction in wet weather. For homes, they are usually built 48″ wide, or at least as wide as the door and walk they serve. A landing should be used to divide flights of steps more than 5′ high. It is recommended that landings be no less than 3′ deep, with the top landing no more than 7-1/2″ below the threshold of the door. To assure proper drainage, the steps should pitch forward with a slope of approximately 1/4″ per foot.

The height of the riser and depth of the tread are important factors for achieving maximum safety and convenience. Use the following riser/tread proportion chart when building steps.

When Riser Is:	Tread Should Be:
4″ to 4-1/2″	18″ to 19″
5″ to 5-1/2″	16″ to 17″
6″ to 6-1/2″	14″ to 15″
7″ to 7-1/2″	10″ to 11″

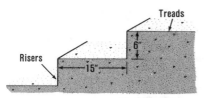

It should be noted that riser and tread size ultimately depends on step use. For a stepped ramp walkway on a long slope, the riser height should be limited to 6″ and the slope between 1/8″ per foot and 1/4″ per foot. In general, wide treads are compatible with a short rise because it allows for a more natural walking stride. Risers and treads must be uniform in any given flight of stairs.

Tools and Materials

QUIKRETE® Concrete Mix or QUIKRETE® 5000 High Early Strength Concrete Mix
QUIKRETE® Acrylic Concrete Cure & Seal
Sand or gravel (for fill), oil or release agent, 5-ply plywood (for side forms), 2 x 4 and 2 x 8 lumber (for forms and stakes), and double-headed nails
Shovel, rake, wheelbarrow, mixing box or power mixer (depending on size of job), saw, hammer, tape measure, string level, finishing trowel, wood float, edger, and darby

PREPARING THE BASE

Level the area to be covered by the steps. Clear it of dirt and stones, as well as grass and other organic material. Dig to a depth of 6″. Use sand or gravel to bring the site to uniform grade, then compact it by dampening and tamping it down. The base should be solid, uniform, and free of foreign matter. Then, go on to build the forms.

BUILDING THE FORMS

1. Use 1/2″ sheets of 5-ply plywood or 2″ lumber to build the side forms. Cut the forms according to the planned dimensions of the steps, always allowing extra depth for fill below the ground level.

2. Brace firmly in place with 2 x 4 stakes and diagonal braces running from the top edge of the sides to stakes set firmly in the ground.

3. Use a level to keep the forms perfectly vertical. If the steps are being built against a house or other foundation,

be sure to apply a 1/2″ mastic expansion joint.

4. Coat the inside surfaces of the forms with oil or release agent to make removal easier.

5. For variations on building forms, see the illustrations.

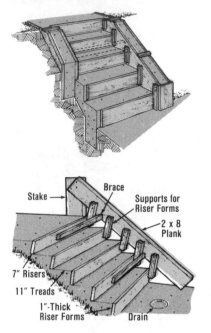

Stake → Brace
Supports for Riser Forms
2 x 8 Plank
7″ Risers
11″ Treads
1″-Thick Riser Forms　Drain

POURING THE CONCRETE AND FINISHING THE SURFACE

1. Fill in any low areas in the forms with gravel, broken brick, or chunks of concrete block; this will also reduce the amount of concrete mix needed. Work the mix in and around all rubble thoroughly. Make sure the rubble is placed back from the form sides so it will not break through the concrete surface.

2. It is important to mix the entire project at one time. Overfill the forms slightly, then work the concrete in and out with

a shovel to compact the mix and eliminate air pockets.

3. Once the mix has been poured and compacted, screed the surface immediately.

4. Use a float or darby to level any remaining ridges and fill any voids in the concrete.

5. Once the surface has turned dull, use an edging tool with a 1/2″ radius to round the edges.

6. Use a trowel to give the concrete a final smoothing. Keep the trowel pressed flat against the surface. Sweep it back and forth in an arc, with each pass overlapping half of the previous lap. To produce a textured, non-skid surface, use a wood float for the final troweling.

CURING THE CONCRETE

Cure the concrete with QUIKRETE® Acrylic Concrete Cure & Seal. When it has fully cured, remove the side forms. Keep in mind that proper curing of all concrete mixes is essential in order for maximum strength to be achieved.

RAMPS

Ramps can be used in the event of a slight change in elevation; they also come in handy as paths for wheelbarrows, lawn mowers, and other equipment. The only addition to the materials list is 1/2″ plywood. Use the plywood for the forms and be sure to stake them securely. Starting at the bottom, pour partially stiff QUIKRETE® Concrete Mix into the forms. Use a trowel to fill in the form, smoothing the surface as you go. Be sure to use partially stiff concrete; if it is too runny, it will not fill the forms completely. Cure the concrete with QUIKRETE® Acrylic Concrete Cure & Seal. Be sure to get permission from your local municipality before cutting away any part of a curb.

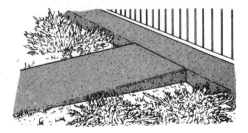

Setting Posts

QUIKRETE® Fast-Setting Concrete firmly sets wood or metal posts in the ground quickly and easily. It is ideal for fence and mailbox posts, flag posts, playground equipment, and lamp and sign posts. QUIKRETE® Fast-Setting Concrete sets in approximately 20 to 40 minutes. Heavy objects, such as basketball backboards, may be hung from the post in 4 hours. (If the temperature is below 72 degrees, additional time for curing will be required.)

For heavy load-bearing applications, use QUIKRETE® Fast-Setting Concrete and QUIK-TUBE™ Building Forms (see page 20).

Tools and Materials

QUIKRETE® Fast-Setting Concrete
QUIKRETE® All-Purpose Gravel or crushed stone
QUIK-TUBE™ Building Form
Plumb line or level
Shovel or post hole digger
Wood preservative and/or rust inhibitor
Wood braces and nails (if needed)

1. The diameter of the posthole should be 3 times the post diameter. Hole depth should be 1/3 the overall post length, plus 6″ for the gravel base. When the post is to be used for structural support, such as for decking, the hole must extend at least 6″ below the frost line. When installing basketball backboard poles or other equipment that requires a solid footing for safe use, follow the manufacturer's recommendations concerning mounting hole depth and size.

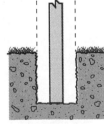

Three Times Diameter of Pole and 1/3 Length.

Tamp Bottom and Sides to Firm.

Place 6″ of Gravel in Hole

2. Tamp the sides and bottom of the hole until firm and place 6″ of QUIKRETE® All-Purpose Gravel or crushed stone in the hole to aid in drainage.

3. Position the post, checking that it is level and plumb.

4. Pour the Fast-Setting Concrete Mix dry from the bag into the hole until it reaches 3" to 4" from the top. Recheck the post for plumb and brace as needed.

5. Pour water onto the dry mix and allow it to soak in. Depending on soil conditions, you will need about 1 gallon of water for each 50lb. bag of Fast-Setting Concrete Mix placed in the hole (QUIK-TUBE™ Building Forms may also be used).

6. Fill the remainder of the hole with soil dug from the hole.

7. QUIKRETE® Fast-Setting Concrete sets in 20 to 40 minutes. Wait 4 hours before applying heavy loads to the post, such as a basketball backboard. (If the temperature is below 72 degrees, additional time for curing will be required.)

8. For holes over 2-1/2' in depth, fill with mix to a depth of 2-1/2' or less and add the appropriate amount of water. Wait until the water soaks all the way into the mix. Then add the remainder of the mix and water.

For Best Results

Use pressure-treated lumber or apply creosote equivalent to prevent below-ground rot. Coat metal posts with rust inhibitor before installing.

Dig larger, dish-shaped holes for posts set in loose or sandy soil.

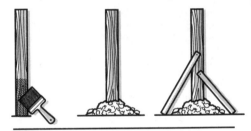

Gallery of Post-Setting Projects

Stable wooden and metal posts and support pieces set in QUIKRETE® Fast-Setting Concrete Mix form the backbone of dozens of successful, useful, and enjoyable home projects.

Fence and Trellis Designs

Perhaps the most popular home project involving the setting of posts is fence building. All fences, from simple two-rail designs to more elaborate split-rail and picket designs, need solid support.

Tools and Materials

Fence posts are available in 4" × 4", 6" × 6", or 8" × 8" sizes cut to any desired length. Rails are usually 2" × 4" lumber cut to 6', 8', or 10' lengths. Fence pickets, capping rails, and other decorative pieces are readily available at any reputable lumberyard.

In addition to the tools outlined under *Setting Posts*, you'll need the following: auger or clamshell digger, measuring tape, string, stakes, saw, hammer, nails, and gate hardware.

PLANNING

1. Before beginning work, check with local authorities to see if there are any ordinances, regulations, or zoning laws concerning the height, location, and materials for fences in your locality. Your property deed may also contain restrictions concerning the construction of fences.

2. Be absolutely certain of your property lines; have the area surveyed if necessary. If you mistakenly build a fence on a neighbor's property, the fence is his, and he has the right to remove it, paint it, etc.

3. It is best to let your neighbors know what you are planning. If you and a neighbor agree to construct a fence centered on your common property line, have a written agreement drawn up and registered by a lawyer concerning the division of construction and maintenance costs. The agreement should bind future owners to the same conditions in case you or your neighbor would move away.

PLOTTING THE FENCE

1. Plot the line of the fence to avoid major visible obstacles such as trees and boulders, and also make sure you are away from all underground utilities before digging postholes. In most cases, a call to your phone, gas, cable, and/or electric company will prompt a free visit to your property to make any necessary alterations.

2. Measure the fence's overall length, allowing space for one or more gates if desired. Divide this length into equal intervals of 6', 8', or 10'. In this way standard precut lumber can be used for the crossrails, minimizing cutting waste. If one section is smaller, consider using it as a gate location.

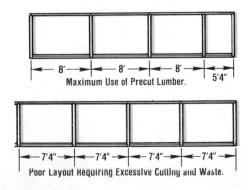

Maximum Use of Precut Lumber.

Poor Layout Requiring Excessive Cutting and Waste.

3. To find the exact post locations, mark both end points of the fence with wooden stakes and run a line between them. Locate positions for all posts between the end posts by measuring intervals with a tape, or by laying out the precut rails in line along the ground.

SETTING POSTS

1. Dig the postholes vertically straight and in the correct locations, using a hand or power auger if the soil is free of stones, or a clamshell-type digger if the soil is rocky.

2. Set the first end post on its gravel base, and pour a collar of QUIKRETE® Fast-Setting Concrete Mix. Use a carpenter's level and plumb bob to align the post 90° vertically.

3. Set the second end post firmly on its gravel base, but do not immediately pour concrete in its hole. Run a string between the tops of these two posts, and then position the interval posts, carefully aligning and bracing them vertically. Make sure the posts are correctly spaced and that the tops of all posts are level with one another.

4. Mix and pour collars of QUIKRETE® Fast-Setting Concrete Mix for all remaining posts. Double-check for plumbness. Allow the concrete to cure 3 to 4 days before adding the rails and facing.

FINISHING

1. Attach the top rail or stringer first. This rail is usually placed flat on top of posts to keep the fence in alignment.

2. Various types of butt, lap, dado, and mortise-and-tenon joints can be used to fasten rails to posts.

3. With the top rail in place, measure down the post to position bottom and middle rails. Before attaching rails to posts, apply paint or wood preservative to cut ends of the lumber.

4. Facing can be done with wood patterns, pickets, wire screen, or solid panels.

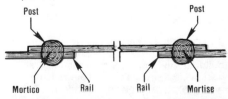

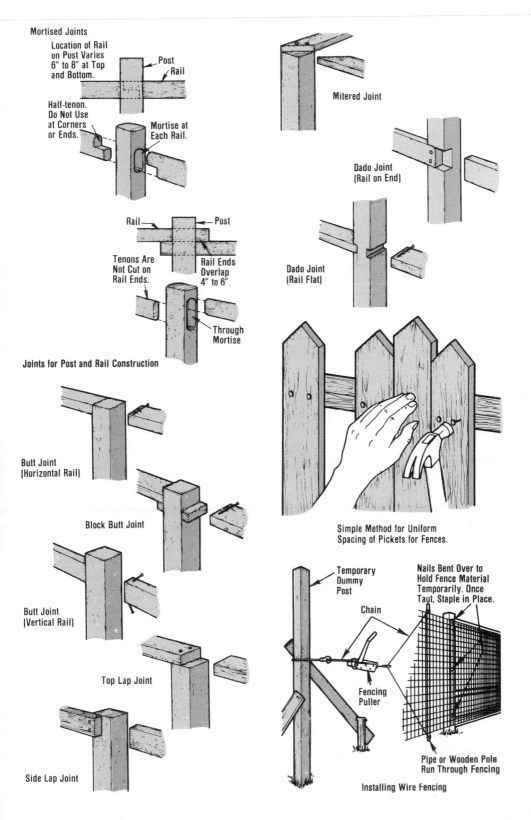

Mortised Joints

Location of Rail on Post Varies 6" to 8" at Top and Bottom.

Post
Rail

Half-tenon. Do Not Use at Corners or Ends.

Mortise at Each Rail.

Rail
Post

Tenons Are Not Cut on Rail Ends.

Rail Ends Overlap 4" to 6".

Through Mortise

Joints for Post and Rail Construction

Butt Joint (Horizontal Rail)

Block Butt Joint

Butt Joint (Vertical Rail)

Top Lap Joint

Side Lap Joint

Mitered Joint

Dado Joint (Rail on End)

Dado Joint (Rail Flat)

Simple Method for Uniform Spacing of Pickets for Fences.

Temporary Dummy Post

Chain

Fencing Puller

Nails Bent Over to Hold Fence Material Temporarily. Once Taut, Staple in Place.

Pipe or Wooden Pole Run Through Fencing

Installing Wire Fencing

For Best Results

If the ground is not level, make sure that you account for differences so that the fence is even. The ground should be built up and cut back so as not to give a choppy appearance.

On severely sloping ground, be sure to erect posts plumb to one another and then tilt the rails as needed to follow the slope. Tilting the rails changes the lengths required to span posts, so make sure you don't come up short when using standard lengths of lumber.

Wrong

Right

Fencing Slightly Uneven Terrain.

Fencing Severe Slopes.

TRELLISES

A trellis to support perennial vines or roses can make a handsome addition to any garden, patio, or landscaped area. Trellises can stand alone, against a building or entranceway, or as part of a fence/windbreak construction.

Although young vines start out quite slender and fragile, by the end of the growing season they can be extremely heavy and full. Use posts of the dimensions used in fence construction, and attach sturdy rail and crosspieces.

For Best Results

Treat the trellis with nontoxic wood preservative (never creosote).

Apply three coats of quality outdoor paint. Consider matching the color of your house or that of the vine blossoms.

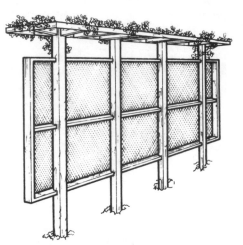

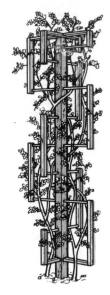

Cast Posts

QUIKRETE® Fiber-Reinforced Concrete can be cast into easy-to-make forms to create a variety of post designs. The fibers provide greater strength to resist chipping and cracking, without sacrificing a nice, smooth finish. And while QUIKRETE® Fiber-Reinforced Concrete is the first choice for making cast posts, QUIKRETE® 5000 or QUIKRETE® Concrete Mix also work well. Note that cast posts can have their own bases or be set in concrete.

Tools and Materials

QUIKRETE® Fiber-Reinforced
Concrete, QUIKRETE® 5000 or
QUIKRETE® Concrete Mix
1/4" plywood or boards for forms,
  decorative molding strips, and nails
Oil or concrete release agent
Square trowel or straightedge
1/2" threaded rod
1/2" steel reinforcing rod (if needed)
Conduit and hardware (as needed)

1. Make wooden forms carefully, using a
   minimum of parts so stripping will be
   easy. Coat all concrete-contact surfaces with oil or concrete release
   agent.

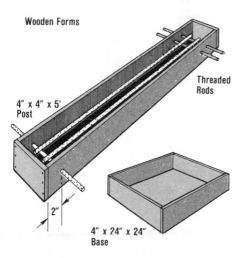

Wooden Forms

Threaded
Rods

4" x 4" x 5'
Post

2"

4" x 24" x 24"
Base

2. Pour freshly mixed QUIKRETE® Fiber-
   Reinforced Concrete, QUIKRETE®
   5000 or Concrete Mix into the forms,
   leveling with a square trowel or
   straightedge. Fill the form completely.

3. Let stand for at least 48 hours before
   removing the forms. Moist-cure for 3
   to 4 days as described earlier.

For Best Results

Use wood moldings to create more
stylish posts.

Install 1/2" reinforcement rods when
making solid posts.

Install conduit or pipe in posts that
will contain electrical cables.

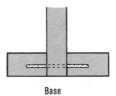

Base

Install any brackets, bolts, studs,
hinges, light fixtures, hangers, etc.,
before the concrete has set.

Portable Posts

Portable posts have a number of uses,
including clothesline posts, tetherball
posts, and supports for badminton or vol-
leyball nets. They are easily made with a
heavy-gauge steel pole, a pipe sleeve
(with an inside diameter equal to the outside diameter of the pole), QUIK-TUBE™
building forms, and a base made from
QUIKRETE® Fast-Setting Concrete Mix.

Tools and Materials

QUIKRETE® Fast-Setting Concrete
  Mix
QUIK-TUBE™ form
Heavy-gauge steel pole and pipe
  sleeve
Square-faced shovel, trowel, tamper,
  tire, and plywood sheet (optional)

1. Sink a QUIK-TUBE™ of the appropriate diameter into the ground, so that
   its top surface is just below grade. Be
   sure that the base it rests on is firm
   and level. (If desired, you can set the
   pole and sleeve directly into a
   concrete-filled hole in the ground.)

2. Position the pipe sleeve and pole in
   the center of the QUIK-TUBE™ form,
   then fill the form with QUIKRETE®
   Fast-Setting Concrete Mix. Make sure
   that the pole is plumb.

Another approach utilizes a discarded
automobile tire as a permanent, above-
grade form. This design supplies ample

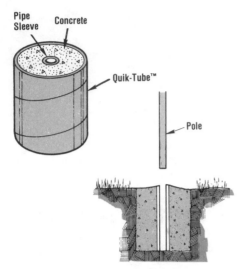

Pipe Sleeve   Concrete

Quik-Tube™

Pole

and more malleable than concrete. This allows it to be cast in smaller dimensions. A bolt set in the base allows disassembly for easy storage.

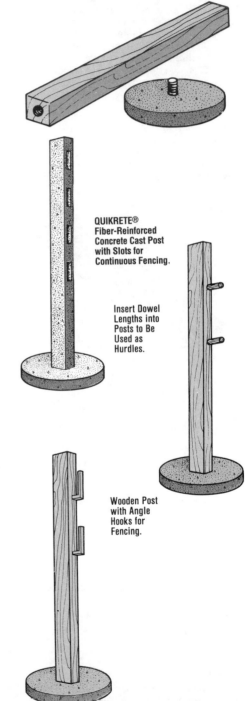

QUIKRETE® Fiber-Reinforced Concrete Cast Post with Slots for Continuous Fencing.

Insert Dowel Lengths into Posts to Be Used as Hurdles.

Wooden Post with Angle Hooks for Fencing.

rigidity, and can be easily moved by tilting the post and rolling it about on the tire.

1. Place the tire on firm, level ground or on a sheet of plywood.

2. Center the post or sleeve and pour QUIKRETE® Fast-Setting Concrete Mix around it.

3. Tamp enough concrete to fill the tire completely. Use enough concrete to slope the top surface so that it drains water.

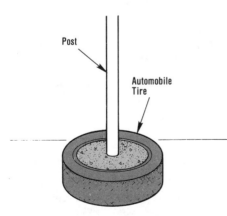

Post

Automobile Tire

A wooden or cast post mounted on a concrete base is a design capable of numerous uses as temporary fencing, including party lawn dividers, crowd-control barricades, hurdles, horse jumps, cattle pens, and so on. QUIKWALL® is a good choice because it weighs as much as concrete, but its fiber reinforcing makes it less brittle as well as stronger

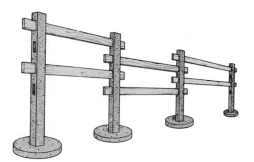

Cast Concrete Projects

QUIKRETE® Fiber-Reinforced Concrete, because of its high strength and smooth surface finish, is the best choice for the cast projects that follow. In addition QUIKRETE® Sand Mix and QUIKWALL® Surface Bonding Cement are flexible enough to be used in a variety of cast projects. For even greater sculpturability with thin projects, QUIKRETE® Quick-Setting Cement is ideal. Its fast setting time allows it to be removed from the form and either carved with a utility knife or worked in some other fashion.

While 2 × 4s are most commonly used to build forms for concrete slabs and walls, cast projects use a wide range of form materials. In addition to QUIK-TUBE™ building forms, tin cans, buckets, cardboard boxes, mailing tubes, and automobile tires can be used to create useful indoor and outdoor accessories. You can also create interesting effects depending on the specific form material you use. For example, unplaned or resawed lumber leaves a wood grain effect on the concrete, while lining the form with heavy kraft paper or plastic produces a smooth finish.

For Best Results

Use double-headed nails when building temporary wood forms. Drive the nails to the first head only, leaving the second head exposed for easy removal.

When working with any type of wood form, apply a thin coating of engine oil to the form before pouring the concrete. This will allow the concrete to set more easily, while reducing the chance of damaging the concrete when it is removed from the form.

Always give a cast project plenty of time to cure before attempting to remove it.

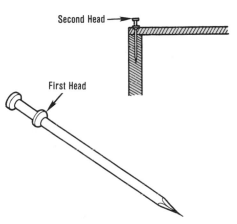

When removing a cast project from a form, do so very carefully. Place it in the shade on a platform that allows for air space underneath the project. Cover with burlap or a thick layer of newspaper and keep this covering wet for at least one week.

As an added touch, cast projects can be painted, stained, or coated with plastic, aluminum, or steel for a metallic effect.

BOOKENDS

Here's a project that's great for the scout in your family or anyone else—sturdy concrete bookends.

Tools and Materials

QUIKRETE® Fiber-Reinforced Concrete, QUIKRETE® Sand Mix, QUIKWALL® Surface Bonding Cement, or QUIKRETE® Quick-Setting Cement
QUIKRETE® Deco Pebbles (optional)
Coffee tin, felt, wood divider, and trowel

1. Place a tight-fitting wood divider into a 2- or 3-lb. coffee tin as shown.

2. Pour the QUIKRETE® Fiber-Reinforced Concrete, QUIKRETE® Sand Mix, QUIKWALL® Surface

Bonding Cement, or QUIKRETE® Quick-Setting Cement into the tin, filling it completely.

3. Use a trowel to smooth and level the surface of the concrete.

4. When the concrete has cured completely, cut away the tin.

5. If QUIKRETE® Deco Pebbles or other aggregates were used in the concrete, scrub and buff the surface of the bookends to bring out the decorative effect.

6. Finally, glue a piece of heavy felt to the bottom of each bookend to avoid scratching shelves and furniture.

ANCHORS

An anchor was never this easy to make; just follow these step-by-step directions.

Tools and Materials

QUIKRETE® Fiber-Reinforced Concrete, QUIKRETE® Sand Mix, or QUIKWALL® Surface Bonding Cement
QUIK-TUBE™ form
Anchor bolt, rebar, and trowel

1. A QUIK-TUBE™ building form is perfect for this project. An old bucket, a large can, or a similar container can also be used.

2. Pour QUIKRETE® Fiber-Reinforced Concrete, QUIKRETE® Sand Mix, or QUIKWALL® Surface Bonding Cement into the form, filling it completely. After about 20 to 30 minutes, place an anchor bolt and rebar in the concrete as shown. Trowel the surface smooth.

3. Do not attempt to use the anchor until the concrete has cured completely. If a QUIK-TUBE™ form was used, cut and peel it away. If a different container was used, it will remain as part of the anchor.

4. If additional weight is needed, make several anchors and join them with chain.

DECORATIVE PLAQUES

Decorative plaques with raised or recessed surfaces are as functional as they are attractive. They are great for flower bed edging or garden accents. When used as edging, partially bury the plaques to secure them; no separate footer or anchoring is required.

Tools and Materials

QUIKRETE® Fiber-Reinforced Concrete, QUIKRETE® Sand Mix, QUIKWALL® Surface Bonding Cement, or QUIKRETE® Quick-Setting Cement
QUIKRETE® Play Sand®
Plywood, 1 × 2 wood strips, saw (keyhole, saber, or jigsaw), and trowel

The mold shown is a direct relief mold made of damp or oiled QUIKRETE® Play Sand on a sheet of plywood. It forms a negative image of the final textured surface of the plaque. The sides of the mold are made of 1 × 2 pieces of wood, and the sand is placed inside and shaped using a variety of sculpting tools.

Strips of wood or rigid foam can also be placed in the mold to create recessed

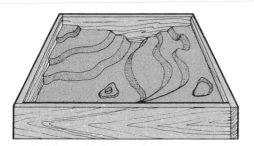

shapes or lettering. For raised or embossed shapes, openings must be cut in the base of the mold with a saw. To create a level surface for the embossed areas, place the mold on a plywood sheet or a screeded and compacted bed of sand.

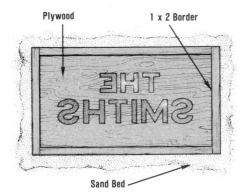

Plywood   1 x 2 Border

THE SMITHS

Sand Bed

Place the QUIKRETE® Fiber-Reinforced Concrete, QUIKRETE® Sand Mix, QUIKWALL® Surface Bonding Cement, or QUIKRETE® Quick-Setting Cement In the mold. Be careful not to disturb the sand or move the rigid foam or wood strips. Smooth the surface of the concrete so that it is level with the upper edges of the sides. Let the concrete set at least 1 full day, then carefully remove the mold. Let the plaque cure for 5 to 7 days.

BOAT LAUNCHING RAMPS

Cast concrete planks make an economical and movable boat launching ramp.

Tools and Materials

QUIKRETE® Fiber-Reinforced Concrete, QUIKRETE® Sand Mix, or QUIKWALL® Surface Bonding Cement
2 × 6 wood, rebar, eye bolts, steel cable, trowel, and broom

After constructing the forms, cut notches as shown for the eye bolts. Pour the QUIKRETE® Fiber-Reinforced Concrete, QUIKRETE® Sand Mix, or QUIKWALL® Surface Bonding Cement, wait about 20 to 30 minutes, then place the rebar and eye bolts in position. Smooth the concrete with a trowel and apply a broomed finish to provide good traction for backing vehicles into the water. Use steel cable to link the finished planks together; this technique will enable them to fit the existing contours of the lake shore or river bank.

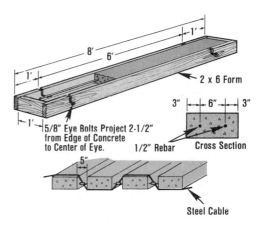

8'   6'   1'

1'   2 x 6 Form

3"   6"   3"

1'   5/8" Eye Bolts Project 2-1/2" from Edge of Concrete to Center of Eye.   1/2" Rebar   Cross Section

5"

Steel Cable

CHIMNEY CAPS

This cast concrete cap will protect your chimney by preventing water from running down next to the flue liner or puddling and freezing on top of the chimney.

Tools and Materials

QUIKRETE® Fiber-Reinforced Concrete, QUIKRETE® Sand Mix, or QUIKWALL® Surface Bonding Cement
2 × 8 wood, cleats, half-round molding, and nails
Metal straps, nuts and bolts, rebar, tape, buckets, trowel, wooden float, edging tool, and plastic sheeting

1. When building the formwork, the inside opening should be sized to the outside dimensions of the chimney walls. Construct the formwork on the ground; it can be hoisted up to the roof when it is completed.

2. Secure cleats across the butted corner joints of the form to increase

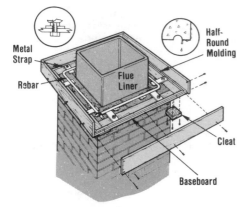

Metal Strap

Rebar

Flue Liner

Half-Round Molding

Cleat

Baseboard

the strength at these points. Lengths of half-round molding, mitered at the corners and tacked in place inside the form, will provide a drip edge along the base of the cap.

3. Hold the form in position on the chimney by bolting metal straps to the base board pieces and overlapping the straps onto the top of the chimney. Install the bolts from the underside, with the securing nut located inside the form.

4. To prevent wet concrete from clogging the nut and bolt threads, size the bolt length carefully so that they do not protrude from the nuts. Also, seal the tops of all nuts with tape before placing the concrete.

5. When choosing the strap material, determine if the straps will be a permanent part of the cap or whether they will be pried out after the formwork is removed. If you plan to leave them in place permanently, be sure to use a metal that will not eventually rust and stain the chimney.

6. When the form is securely in place on the chimney, install rebar over the straps as shown.

7. Mix the QUIKRETE® Fiber-Reinforced Concrete, QUIKRETE® Sand Mix, or QUIKWALL® Surface Bonding Cement. Do the mixing on the ground and pass the concrete up to the roof 1 bucket at a time.

8. Layer the concrete evenly on all sides of the flue to help stabilize the form. Loading one side of the form while the opposite side is empty will cause it to tip forward.

9. When the form is completely full, let the concrete stiffen slightly before beginning to build up the drainage

slope away from the flue liner. Use a wooden float to build up the slope, working from the outside edge of the form to the flue wall. Also, form a small radius curve along the edges of the form using an edging tool.

10. Wet down the surfaces of the cap and cover it with plastic sheeting to prevent water loss.

11. The formwork can be carefully removed within 1 or 2 days. Curing will take approximately 5 to 7 days.

DOWNSPOUT SPLASH GUARDS

A concrete downspout splash guard is durable, long-lasting, and easy to build with these step-by-step directions.

Tools and Materials

QUIKRETE® Fiber-Reinforced Concrete, QUIKRETE® Sand Mix, QUIKWALL® Surface Bonding Cement, or QUIKRETE® Quick-Setting Cement

Crushed stone or gravel, 1 × 4 forming lumber, stakes, nails, shovel, and trowel

1. Dig a trench the required length; it should be approximately 12" wide and 6" deep.

2. Use 1 × 4 lumber to build the forms. Stake and nail boards firmly in place, then apply a thin coating of engine oil to the form.

3. Pour QUIKRETE® Fiber-Reinforced Concrete, QUIKRETE® Sand Mix, QUIKWALL® Surface Bonding Cement, or QUIKRETE® Quick-Setting Cement into the form. Use a trowel to shape the gutter as shown; it should be at least 4" deep at its deepest point. Allow at least 1 week curing time before using.

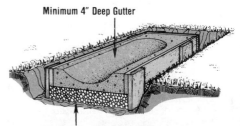

Minimum 4" Deep Gutter

Crushed Stone or Gravel Base

4. Be certain to always slope the gutter away from the downspout in order to maintain proper drainage.

GARDEN EDGING/CURBING

To accentuate your home's exterior, try this project—garden edging/curbing.

Tools and Materials

QUIKRETE® Fiber-Reinforced Concrete, QUIKRETE® Sand Mix, or QUIKWALL® Surface Bonding Cement
1 × 2 lumber and trowel

1. Construct a V-shaped form from 1 × 2s; a good workable length is 4', although this can vary.

2. As shown in the cross section, the form should be approximately 10" high and at least 4" wide at its widest point, which will eventually be the base of the edging. Making the base any narrower will cause the edging/curbing to be too unstable.

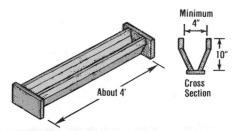

Minimum
4"

10"

About 4'

Cross Section

3. Apply a thin coating of engine oil to the form. Pour QUIKRETE® Fiber-Reinforced Concrete, QUIKRETE® Sand Mix, or QUIKWALL® Surface Bonding Cement into the form, filling it completely. Trowel the surface smooth, then allow at least 48 hours curing time before removing it from the form.

4. If you want to stake the edging/curbing into the ground, simply cast the project with holes in the center as shown.

Property Markers

When Mason and Dixon placed their survey markers along the Pennsylvania-Maryland border in 1767, they were clearly identifiable as well as accurate. A boundary dispute is one of the most vexing situations that can confront a property owner, and many disputes are the result of survey features having changed over the years, pins that have been partially covered or buried by overgrown weeds, or stakes that have been removed because they were not recognized as survey marks.

Cast concrete markers that are 4" × 4" are solid, durable, noticeable and, because they are clearly identifiable as markers, unlikely to be accidentally removed.

Tools and Materials

QUIKRETE® Fiber-Reinforced Concrete Mix
1/2" plywood (32" × 10" per form)
Oil or concrete release agent
Wire

MARKERS

1. Cut the plywood into eight sections with the following dimensions: 5" × 10" (2); 4" × 10" (2); 4" × 6" (2); and 3" × 6" (2).

2. Center the 3" × 6" pieces on the 5" × 10"s and the 4" × 6" pieces on the 4" × 10"s. Glue or tack the pieces together to make sides for the form.

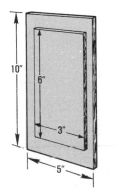

10"

6"

3"

5"

Side

3. Coat the interiors with a thin film of oil or a release agent.

4. Fit the sides together and bind them at the top and bottom with the wire.

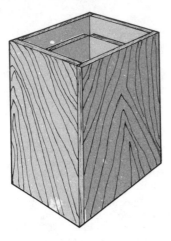

5. Fill the form with the prepared concrete mix; poke a stick, broom handle, or similar object into the form to compact the concrete and remove any air pockets. Screed the concrete flush with the form.

6. Allow the concrete to cure for at least a day before removing the form.

For Best Results

After the concrete has received its initial set, customize the marker cap with the date of installation, survey, and the owners' names.

Cast Concrete Planters

In this project, you'll learn to build both a rectangular and a round planter.

RECTANGULAR PLANTER

Tools and Materials

QUIKRETE® Fiber-Reinforced Concrete, QUIKRETE® Sand Mix, QUIKWALL® Surface Bonding Cement, or QUIKRETE® Quick-Setting Cement
3/4″ plywood, drill, dowel, cardboard box or similar container, tamper, and oil

1. Use 3/4″ plywood to build the forms according to the following outside dimensions: 18″ long × 15″ wide × 10″ high.

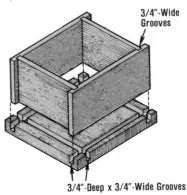

3/4″-Wide Grooves

3/4″-Deep x 3/4″-Wide Grooves

2. Assemble the form by means of a groove system as shown in the illustration. Cut the grooves 3/4″ deep × 3/4″ wide; for extra rigidity, the sides and ends can be held together with strong cord. To use the groove system, the base lumber must be at least 1-1/2″ thick.

3. Drill a 1/2″ hole through the center of the bottom, then plug it with an oiled dowel that is long enough to penetrate the casting. The dowel will act as a drain hole for the casting.

4. Prepare the inner form by filling a cardboard box, a large can, or even a wastebasket with sand. For a double-cavity planter, use two containers. Do not put the inner form in place until after the concrete base has been poured.

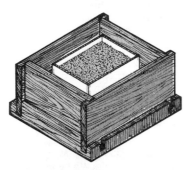

5. To make removing the form easier, coat the inside with a thin layer of oil.

6. To cast the planter, pour the base layer of concrete, add the inner form, then fill in around it. Use a tamper to firm the concrete around the form as the pouring progresses.

7. When the concrete has set, remove the form. Clean the form parts immediately after removing them, then set them aside for future use. (They must always be re-oiled before each use.) Allow the concrete to cure 3 to 4 days before using the planter.

8. To add color and durability, consider using QUIKRETE® liquid Cement Colors or painting the planter with QUIKRETE® Masonry Coating.

ROUND PLANTER

Tools and Materials

QUIKRETE® Fiber-Reinforced Concrete, QUIKRETE® Sand Mix, QUIKWALL® Surface Bonding Cement, or QUIKRETE® Quick-Setting Cement
QUIK-TUBE™ form
Sand, wastebasket or similar container, drill, dowel, inner form, oil, and tamper

1. Round planters can be cast in a pile of damp sand; building wood forms is not necessary. Scoop out an approximate-sized hole in the sand, then use a wastebasket, drum, or similar container to complete the cavity.

2. Compact the sand around the container. As you bear down on the container, twist it to make a good impression. When removing the container, twist it as you lift.

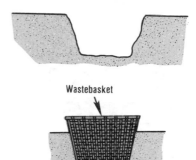

Wastebasket

3. Pour some of the mix to form the base, then insert an oiled dowel to form the drain hole as shown. Make sure the dowel is long enough to penetrate the casting.

4. A QUIK-TUBE™ form is an ideal choice for the inner form. It should be smaller than the container used to form the cavity.

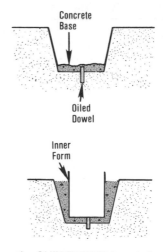

Concrete Base

Oiled Dowel

Inner Form

5. When the QUIK-TUBE™ form is in place, pour the remaining concrete around it. Use a tamper to compact the concrete around the form while you pour.

6. Wet-cure the planter in the sand for 3 to 4 days.

7. To add color and durability, consider QUIKRETE® Liquid Cement Colors or painting the planter with QUIKRETE® Masonry Coating.

Anchoring Projects

QUIKRETE® Anchoring Cement expands as it cures to become stronger than ordinary concrete when mounting or anchoring objects in concrete or masonry. Depending on the amount of water used, QUIKRETE® Anchoring Cement can be poured like syrup or worked like putty. It normally sets in 10 to 30 minutes. After an hour or so, QUIKRETE® Anchoring Cement will have set sufficiently to screw most types of anchor bolts home. For extreme loads, wait 2 hours before applying load to the anchor. Within 24 hours, QUIKRETE® Anchoring Cement reaches a pull-out strength of 12,500 psi (for 1/2″ bolts embedded 8″ in 4,000 psi concrete).

FLOOR MOUNTINGS

Anchoring Cement's exceptional strength and quick-setting characteristics are ideal for fastening heavy-duty industrial machinery. But its simple application makes it just as desirable for home use in projects such as anchoring bolts, posts, wrought-iron railing, signs, workshop machines, and door stops.

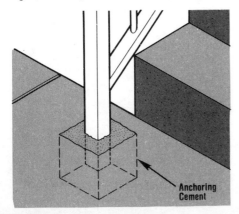

Anchoring Cement

For floor mountings and other horizontal applications, prepare the QUIKRETE® Anchoring Cement to a pourable consistency by mixing 4-to-5 parts cement with 1 part water.

Tools and Materials

QUIKRETE® Anchoring Cement
QUIKRETE® Acrylic Concrete Cure & Seal
Star drill and hammer or 1/2″ electric drill with masonry bit
Small brush

ANCHORING

1. Mark the location of the holes for the bolts.

2. Make a hole at least 1″ larger than the diameter of the object to be anchored. For large objects, such as metal pipes or fence posts, use a diamond-edge cold chisel and a small sledgehammer to make the hole. The hole must be at least 2″ deep.

3. Brush all dirt, dust, and other loose material from the hole. Dampen the interior of the hole.

4. Insert the object to be anchored and pour the prepared mix into the hole to the surface level. Anchoring Cement can also be packed in with a trowel; when using this method, be sure to completely fill the hole.

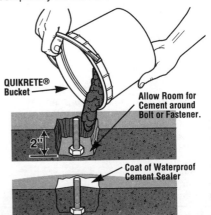

QUIKRETE® Bucket

Allow Room for Cement around Bolt or Fastener.

2″

Coat of Waterproof Cement Sealer

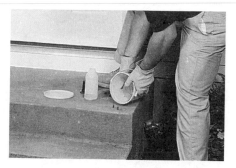

5. Hold the object being anchored in place until the mix begins to stiffen. This will depend on the amount of water used to prepare the mix.

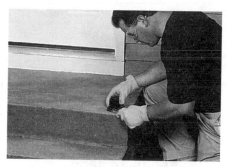

6. Wait about 45 minutes before fastening anything to the bolt or post to allow the mix time to achieve a final set.

For Best Results

Use only clean water and containers to prepare the mix.

Apply a coat of QUIKRETE® Acrylic Concrete Cure & Seal to all outside projects or areas exposed to dampness or moisture after the mix obtains a final set.

Use QUIKRETE® Concrete and Asphalt Cleaner to make certain that any oil or other film that could prevent bonding has been cleaned from the hole.

WALL MOUNTINGS

QUIKRETE® Anchoring Cement's quick setup time and great strength make it the ideal choice for a wide range of vertical anchoring projects, including bolts, brackets, hooks, racks, shelves, pulleys, and awning and canopy mounts. For vertical installations, decrease the amount of water in the mix so it reaches a putty-like texture.

Tools and Materials

QUIKRETE® Anchoring Cement
QUIKRETE® Acrylic Concrete
  Cure & Seal
Star drill and hammer or 1/2″ electric drill with masonry bit
Small brush and trowel

ANCHORING

1. Mark on the concrete the location of the hole(s) for the hook or mounting bolts.

2. Make a hole at least 2″ deep and at least 1″ larger than the diameter of the bolt or hook to be inserted.

3. Brush all dirt, dust, or other loose material out of the hole.

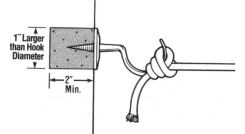

4. Dampen the interior of the hole; leave no standing water. Insert the hook or bolt and pack the prepared mix firmly around it to just above surface level. Prepare only as much mix as can be applied in 10 minutes.

5. Hold the bolt or hook in place until the mix begins to stiffen. (It generally takes only a few minutes. Mix pre-

pared with large amounts of water will take longer.)

6. After all the bolts have set for about 45 minutes, attach any mounting brackets that your project requires. Except for the most unusually heavy objects, mounting can be done after a few hours.

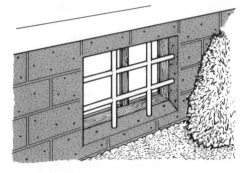

For Best Results

Use only clean containers and potable water to prepare the mix.

For exterior use and areas exposed to dampness or moisture, apply a coat of QUIKRETE® Acrylic Concrete Cure & Seal after the concrete reaches its final set.

Swimming Pool Accessories

QUIKRETE® Hydraulic Water-Stop Cement is the ideal product for anchoring applications that are constantly exposed to water or moisture. Typical examples are swimming pool ladders, diving board mounts, pool slides, and jacuzzi and hot tub accessories. White Hydraulic Water-Stop Cement is available for pool applications when color matching is important.

Like QUIKRETE® Anchoring Cement, QUIKRETE® Hydraulic Water-Stop Cement expands as it cures to form a tight-fitting plug with a high pull-out resistance. But unlike QUIKRETE® Anchoring

Cement, QUIKRETE® Hydraulic Water-Stop Cement is not adversely affected by constant exposure to water.

Tools and Materials

QUIKRETE® White Hydraulic Water-Stop Cement
Star drill and hammer or 1/2" electric drill with masonry bit

---

ANCHORING BASICS

Installation is similar to anchoring with QUIKRETE® Anchoring Cement (see page 54). Mix the QUIKRETE® Hydraulic Water-Stop Cement to a heavy putty-like consistency. A mix ratio of approximately 4-1/2 parts cement to 1 part water should be used.

Position the anchor or bolt and pack the cement into the hole. Work quickly, as the Hydraulic Water-Stop Cement will set in 3 to 5 minutes after mixing. Only mix as much cement as can be used during this time.

DIVING BOARDS, SLIDES, LADDERS, AND RAILS

All diving boards and slides must be installed to the "Suggested Minimum Standards" of the National Swimming Pool Institute (NSPI). Most pool equipment manufacturers adhere to the requirements of the NSPI, so follow their step-by-step installation instructions regarding anchoring hardware and mounting procedures.

Most swimming pool ladders and rails come equipped with coping sockets or the anchor sleeves and base needed for surface mounting. However, these inserts can also be embedded (anchored) below the pool surround surface using QUIK-RETE® Hydraulic Water-Stop Cement.

All of the anchor sockets or inserts that are embedded in concrete have grounding screws as required by the National Electrical Code. This connection acts as a lightning arrester when properly installed. Again, follow the manufacturers' installation instructions precisely to ensure proper protection.

Rip Rap Projects:
Dams, Bulkheads, and Erosion Control Walls

QUIKRETE® Concrete and Sand mixes are packaged in biodegradable paper bags suitable for rip rapping to save time and labor on heavy-duty projects. They are ideal for constructing headwalls for culverts and other erosion control projects, as well as for building dams, beach bulkheads, and waterway walls. They are also especially useful in out-of-the-way locations and eliminate the need for costly construction machinery. A particular advantage in their use is the ability to set in a wide range of conditions, from water immersion to natural moisture alone.

DAMS AND BULKHEADS

A sturdy, long-lasting dam or bulkhead is a relatively quick and simple job with rip rap. The 60-lb. bag is suggested because of its easy handling. When estimating rip rap needs, figure five bags for 7 linear feet and three bags for each vertical foot.

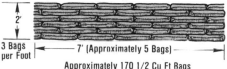

3 Bags per Foot |←——— 7' (Approximately 5 Bags) ———→|

Approximately 170 1/2 Cu Ft Bags Are Needed for a 100 Sq Ft Area.

Tools and Materials

QUIKRETE® Concrete or Sand Mix
Steel reinforcing rods (staple or straight)
Sledgehammer and shovel

CONSTRUCTION

1. Outline the area to be excavated, extending the excavation at least 1' beyond the edge of the planned wall. Remove all grass, roots, and other organic matter. Dig to a depth of 6" and bring the base of this trench to a uniform grade.

2. Lay the first tier of bags for the dam or bulkhead wall by butting the bags together end-to-end. Stack succeeding tiers in an interlocking fashion or bond pattern. Thoroughly sprinkle and tamp each layer of bags. Perforating the bags with a pitchfork or metal rake will speed saturation and initial set.

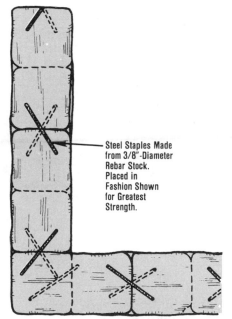

Steel Staples Made from 3/8"-Diameter Rebar Stock. Placed in Fashion Shown for Greatest Strength.

Alternate Directions of Staples from Bag to Bag and Tier to Tier.

3. To increase the wall's strength, 3/8" steel rebar staples can be driven into the bags. Alternate the staple direction from bag to bag and tier to tier.

4. As an alternative, drive straight rebar rods down through the bags as

shown. This method is needed if the bags are stacked under water.

5. Depending on the height of the dam wall and the capacity of the reservoir, it may be desirable to leave channels for water runoff between bags in the top tier.

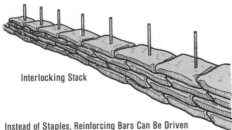

Interlocking Stack

Instead of Staples, Reinforcing Bars Can Be Driven Vertically Through the Bags as They Are Stacked. This Method Will Be Necessary if the Bags Are Stacked Under Water.

For Best Results

The work should be completed with as little interruption as possible to assure integral construction.

Materials should be kept wet for 4 days to assist curing, although natural moisture alone is enough to set.

Walls higher than 10' should be temporarily sway braced with 2 × 4s to facilitate initial set.

Interlocking Dam and Wing Walls

SLOPE WALLS/ EROSION CONTROL

Controlling erosion with rip rap is almost as easy as playing with children's building blocks. Because it will set from natural moisture alone and comes in easy-to-handle bags, erosion walls can be built from rip rap even in locations inaccessible for other construction methods.

Tools and Materials

QUIKRETE® Concrete or Sand Mix
Steel reinforcing rods
Sledgehammer, shovel, rake, and tamper

CONSTRUCTION

1. Place first tier of bags onto a secure base end-to-end.

2. Set back succeeding rows in a stair-step fashion to full height of slope. Set bags in a running bond pattern with the ends butted together and corners interlocked. Anchor the bags to the slope with 3/8" rebar. Perforate and tamp bags as thoroughly as possible.

Set Bags in a Running Bond Pattern with the Ends Butted Together and Corners Interlocked.

3. As each tier is laid, backfill with tamped-in dirt to assure a solid bank.

For Best Results

Drive steel reinforcing rods through each bag to anchor them to the slope.

Avoid doing the job when the temperature is at or near freezing.

Complete the job with as little interruption as possible to assure integral construction.

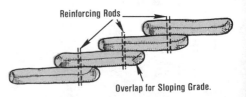

Reinforcing Rods

Overlap for Sloping Grade.

Use 3/8" Rebar to Anchor Bags.

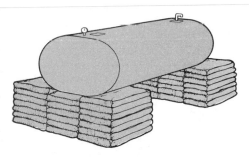

If water is available, keep the material wet for 4 days to assist curing.

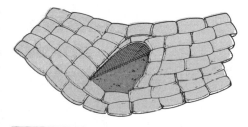

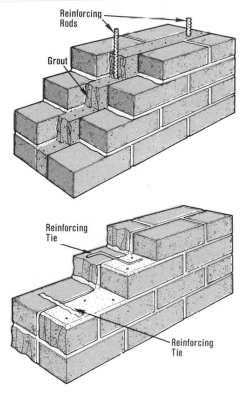

Basic Brick Construction:
Walls, Corners, Pillars and Posts, and Edging

The best way to learn the art of brick-laying is through hands-on experience, and there's no better place to start than with a basic freestanding brick wall. The wall described here is built in the common or American bond pattern, a pattern that is very strong and easy to lay. The wall is built in two wythes or tiers and can be safely built up to 3'; for a wall above 3', steel reinforcement is required. Reinforcing can be either rods inserted into the grout after it has stiffened slightly or ties laid across two wythes to help hold them together. If you are planning to build a wall more than 3' high, it is best to consult your local building codes for exact specifications and techniques.

BRICKLAYING TERMS

Before beginning any of the bricklaying projects, study the following terms and their definitions. This will help you understand the various brick positions and patterns, as well as the typical mortar joints used.

Bull Header. A rowlock brick laid with its longest dimension perpendicular to the face of the wall.
Bull Stretcher. A rowlock brick laid with its longest dimension parallel to the face of the wall.

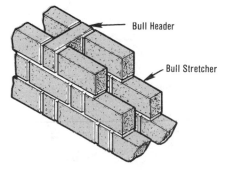

Course. One of the continuous horizontal rows of masonry that, bonded together, forms the masonry structure.

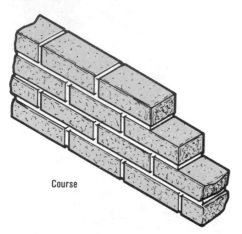

Course

Header. A masonry unit laid flat with its longest dimension perpendicular to the face of the wall. It is generally used to tie two wythes of masonry together.

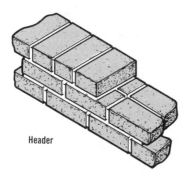

Header

Rowlock. A brick laid on its face, or edge.
Soldier. A brick laid on its end so that its longest dimension is parallel to the vertical axis of the face of the wall.

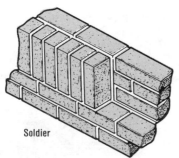

Soldier

Stretcher. A masonry unit laid flat with its longest dimension parallel to the face of the wall.

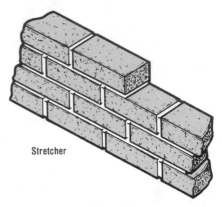

Stretcher

Wythe. A continuous vertical section or thickness of masonry 4" or greater.

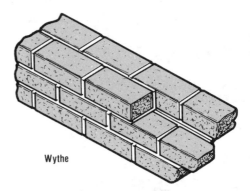

Wythe

BRICK WALLS

Tools and Materials

QUIKRETE® Mortar Mix or Mason Mix Bricks, chalk line, mortarboard, hose, wheelbarrow, trowel, level, carpenter's square, tape measure, brick set, mason's hammer, goggles, jointer, mason's line, and line blocks

SELECTING A SITE

Take time to select a site for your wall; careful location can contribute greatly to the wall's longevity. Choose a spot where the soil is firm and drainage is good. Whenever possible, avoid locating the wall near large trees because the roots can exert great pressure on the wall and easily crack the foundation.

PREPARATION

The first step in building a brick wall is to lay a solid footer or foundation wall. For detailed instructions on pouring a concrete footer or foundation, see *Footers for Walls* (page 11) or *Concrete Walls* (page 13). Be sure to allow the footer or foundation at least two full days to cure before beginning to lay the brick.

Locate your bricks in several stacks along the jobsite; this will save you time and effort later. To prevent the bricks from absorbing too much moisture from the mortar, hose them down a few hours before beginning work. The hose will also come in handy for rinsing your tools occasionally as you work and for keeping the mortar sufficiently moist.

To locate the outer edge of the wall, use a tape measure to measure in from the edge of the foundation at each end. Snap a chalk line between the two points to mark a guideline to keep the wall centered. You are now ready to begin building the wall using the following step-by-step procedure.

PREPARING THE MORTAR

1. Mix the QUIKRETE® Mortar Mix or Mason Mix with water until you obtain a smooth, plastic-like consistency.

2. Make a dry run by laying a course of stretcher bricks along the chalk line for the entire length of the wall. Leave 1/2" between each brick for the head joints and mark the position of the bricks on the foundation with a piece of chalk. Lay this course without cutting any of the bricks; if necessary, adjust the head joint width.

3. Remove the dry course from the foundation, then throw a mortar line on the foundation. To do this, load the trowel with mortar and, as you bring your arm back toward your body, rotate the trowel to deposit the mortar evenly. Mortar should be applied approximately 1" thick, 1 brick wide, and 3 to 4 bricks long. (You might want to practice throwing lines on the mortarboard until you become familiar with the technique.)

4. Furrow the mortar with the point of the trowel. Divide the mortar cleanly

with the trowel; do not scrape it. Good furrows not only ensure that the bricks are laid evenly, but they also help to squeeze out excess mortar on the sides as the bricks are set in place.

LAYING THE BRICKS

1. Lay the first course of stretcher bricks in the mortar. Beginning with the second brick, apply mortar to the head joint end of each brick, then shove the bricks into place firmly so that the mortar is squeezed out of all sides of the joints. Use a level to check the course for correct height, then place it on top to make sure that all the bricks are plumb and level.

2. Make sure that the head joint thicknesses correspond with your chalk marks. When you have to move a brick, tap it gently with the trowel handle; never pull on it because this breaks the bond. Be sure to trim off any excess mortar from the sides of the bricks.

3. Throw another mortar line alongside the first course, then begin laying the second, or backup, course. Use the level to make sure that the two courses are of equal height, but do not mortar them together.

4. Before beginning to lay the second, or header, course, cut two bricks to half length. To cut a brick, lay it on the ground and score it all the way around using a hammer and brick set. Break the brick in two with a sharp blow to the brick set. **Note:** When cutting bricks, protect your eyes by wearing goggles.

5. Use the two half bricks to begin the second, or header, course. This will ensure that the first two courses are staggered for structural purposes.

6. To finish the second course of the lead, lay three header bricks and make sure that they are plumb and level. As seen in the photo, the third and fifth courses consist of stretchers similar to the first course; the fourth course begins with a single header, followed by stretchers. Use the level to make sure that the lead is true on each course.

7. Build another lead on the other end of the foundation. As the mortar begins to set, it is best to stop laying bricks and use a concave jointer to finish the mortar joints. Work along the vertical joints first; this will help make them weatherproof as well as improve the appearance of the wall.

FILLING IN THE LEADS

1. Stretch a mason's line between the completed leads, then begin laying the outer course. The line should be approximately 1/16" away from the bricks and flush with their top edges as shown. Work from both ends of the wall toward the middle. When you reach the final brick, mortar both sides of it and push it straight down to squeeze the mortar out from the joints.

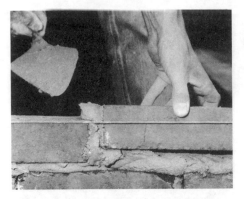

4. To build a higher wall, simply build more five-course leads at each end of the wall. Keep in mind that some type of reinforcing should be used for higher walls.

5. Scoop mortar onto the trowel and use the concave jointer to fill in the joints on the top course. Keep a careful check on the joint thickness as you go. When you have laid the last brick, check the top course for alignment.

2. Move the mason's line to the back of the wall and begin laying the backup course. Remember to check your work with the level for accuracy and finish the joints with the concave jointer when they are almost dry.

3. The fifth, or top, course is laid exactly like the first. Move the mason's line up, throw a mortar line, and begin laying the bricks. Apply a generous amount of mortar on the face of each brick, then shove the brick firmly into place.

3. Lay the four remaining bricks in the first course of the lead. With the level and/or carpenter's square, check the alignment and make sure that the bricks are level and plumb.

BUILDING CORNERS

A wall with corners is not much harder to build than the basic freestanding wall. The following directions show how to build a corner in the common bond pattern, but they can be adapted to any of the other patterns as well.

1. Snap chalk lines on both sides, then check to make sure that they are perfectly square using a carpenter's square or the 3-4-5 method.

4. Throw mortar lines and lay the backup course as shown. Both courses should be level with one another; there is no mortar joint between the two.

2. Make a dry run to mark the position of the bricks. Throw a mortar line, then place the first brick exactly at the corner, being careful to line it up with the chalk lines.

5. To lay the second course, cut two bricks into quarter and three-quarter pieces. Begin by laying the three-quarter brick pieces perpendicular to one another to form the outer edge of the corner. Continue by laying several header bricks out from the corner. Finally, complete the second course by inserting the two quarter closure bricks as shown.

6. Lay courses 3 through 5 to finish the corner lead. Courses 3 and 5 are similar to course 1; course 4 begins with a header positioned as shown.

7. Construct a second lead at the opposite corner.

OTHER TYPES OF BONDS

In addition to the common bond pattern, there are a number of other patterns from which to choose. By using the previous directions for laying the common bond, you can use any of these patterns to give variety to your bricklaying work.

Running Bond. This is the simplest pattern; it consists of only stretchers. Reinforcing ties are usually used with it because of the absence of headers. Running bond is common in brick veneer walls and wall cavity construction.

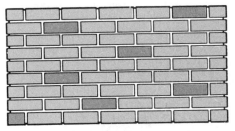

Running Bond

Common or American Bond. As detailed in the step-by-step instructions,

Common Bond

this is a variation of the running bond, with a course of full-length headers placed at regular intervals for structural bonding.

Flemish Bond. This pattern uses alternate stretchers and headers, with the headers in alternate courses centered over the stretchers in the intervening courses.

These joints center on the stretchers themselves.

Stack or Block Bond. This is a weak bond, used normally for decorative effect on veneers. All vertical joints are aligned, and steel reinforcing ties must be installed if the pattern is being used structurally.

Flemish Bond

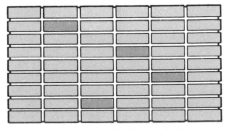

Stack Bond

English Bond. This pattern also uses alternate stretchers and headers, but the headers are centered on the stretchers and the joints between the stretchers. The head joints between the stretchers in all the courses line up vertically.

English Bond

English Cross or Dutch Bond. This is a variation on the English, the only difference being that the vertical joints between the stretchers in alternate courses do not line up vertically.

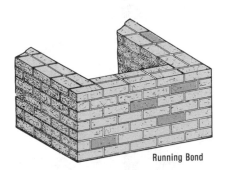

Running Bond

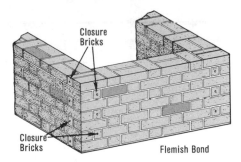

Closure Bricks

Closure Bricks

Flemish Bond

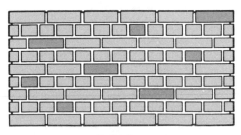

English Cross

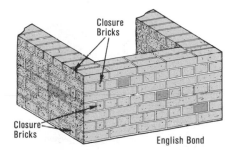

Closure Bricks

Closure Bricks

English Bond

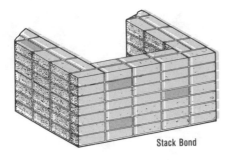

Stack Bond

Struck

Extruded

JOINTS

There are several commonly used methods of finishing mortared joints. Choose a finishing method based on the type of construction. The best joints for strength and waterproofing are concave and V-joints. A weathered joint is also strong and the most watertight. Raked, struck, and extruded joints are perhaps the most dramatic looking; however, they are not very water-resistant. Care should be taken when using them in rainy or freezing climates. A flush joint is the simplest joint—excess mortar is simply cut off with the trowel. But this joint is not particularly strong or water-resistant.

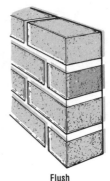

Flush

PILLARS AND POSTS

The first step in making pillars and posts of masonry units is to construct adequate footings.

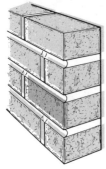

Concave

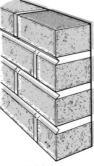

V-Joint

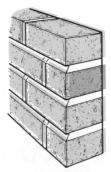

Weathered

Raked

1. Make the forms. If the top surface of the footings will be level with or below the grade, cut the forms directly in the soil. If the surface of the footing will be above grade, use a shallow wood form in conjunction with a cavity cut in the soil.

The Following Figures Illustrate Bond Patterns for Solid Piers. Alternate the Courses as Shown for Narrow Posts.

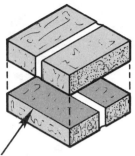

About 8" x 8"

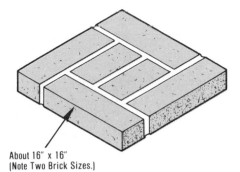

About 16" x 16"
(Note Two Brick Sizes.)

Second. Fourth. Sixth. etc.. Courses

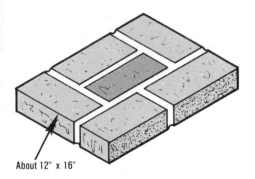

About 12" x 16"

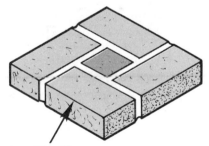

About 12" x 12"

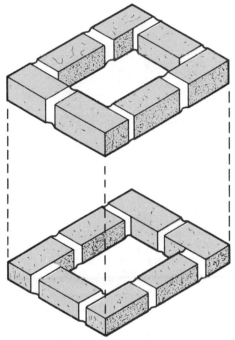

First. Third. Fifth. etc.. Courses

Bond Pattern for a Hollow Pier. Alternate Courses.

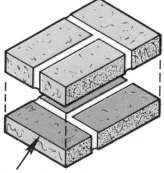

About 8" x 12"

2. Mix QUIKRETE® Concrete Mix and pour it into the form.

3. When all standing water has evaporated, use a trowel to smooth the surface of the footing.

4. Moist-cure the concrete.

Once the footings have set, continue pillar and post construction as you would if you were building a full wall. Use a level frequently to check the horizontal plane of each course and the plumbness

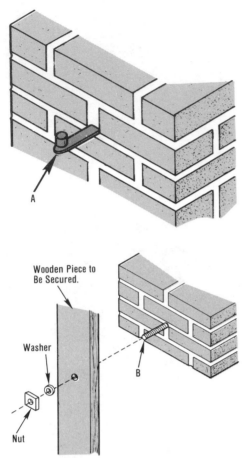

A

Wooden Piece to
Be Secured.

Washer

Nut

B

To Mount a Gate, either (A) Install Hinge Hooks by
Mortaring Them into Joints, or (B) Attach a Wood
Frame to Bolts Mortared into the Post.

of each wall. Use a large carpenter's
square to ensure that the corners are
square. Cap the pillar or post with precast concrete slabs, hand-formed
mounds of QUIKRETE® Concrete or
Mortar, removable wood caps, or pieces
of flagstone.

Typical Post Caps.

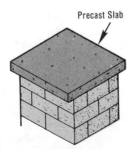

Precast Slab

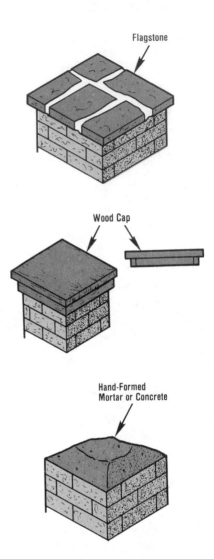

Flagstone

Wood Cap

Hand-Formed
Mortar or Concrete

For Best Results

Be sure that dirt walls are vertical or
that they slant out slightly at the base.

Be sure that the base for the footing is
firm and level.

Check to see that the surface of the
wood form is level.

Add vertical steel reinforcement rods
or conduit for electrical cable.

Add brackets, bolts, studs, hinges,
light fixtures, and/or hangers before
the concrete or masonry has set.

Install the cap at a slight angle so that
it sheds water.

EDGING

Brick edging is the perfect complement to concrete walkways and patios.

1. Stake out the area for the edging using measuring tape and twine. The width of the edging should be equal to the length of the brick being used—usually 8".

2. Remove the sod and soil to a depth equal to the width of the brick—usually about 4".

3. Use one of the bricks to tamp down the excavation and make it as smooth as possible.

4. Prepare the QUIKRETE® Mortar Mix or Mason Mix; then spread a layer in the excavation. This will serve as a foundation for the bricks.

5. Set the bricks in place by applying mortar to one side and pressing each brick firmly against the preceding one.

6. To adjust a brick, tap it with the trowel handle; never pull on it because this breaks the bond. Use the trowel to trim off any excess mortar from the tops of the bricks as you go.

7. With this simple construction technique, you can even make curved edging. Just dig the excavation to the desired curve, taking care to keep the width the same at all times.

Gallery of Brick Projects

Brick Steps

As an alternative to plain concrete steps, bricks can be used as facing over the concrete. Building brick steps involves the same tools and materials as concrete steps, with the following additions: QUIKRETE® Mortar Mix or Mason Mix, bricks, 1/2″ wooden spacer, concave jointer, wooden mallet, mason's line, burlap sack, and stiff broom or brush.

Follow the same procedures that are used for concrete steps to prepare the base, build the forms, pour the concrete, finish the surface, and cure the concrete. You are now ready to lay the bricks in the concrete, using the following procedure:

1. Wet down the bricks several hours before beginning the project; this will prevent them from absorbing too much water from the mortar.

2. Place and screed a 1/2″ thick wet mortar bed between temporary form boards set one brick length apart. Use a special bladed screed to level the concrete. The screed rides on the forms and extends down one brick-thickness below them; the forms should be set for this depth, plus an extra 1/2″ to allow for the mortar bed.

3. As the screed is moved along, place the bricks in the wet concrete, leaving 1/2″ open joints between them. A 1/2″ wooden spacer can be used to ensure that the joints are uniform. Gently tap the bricks with a wooden mallet to set them.

4. Use a trowel to pack the concrete into the joints, then tool the joints with a concave jointer.

5. Wait several hours, then scrub the set bricks with a burlap sack to remove any stains. Once the mortar is dry, brush the surface with a stiff broom or brush to remove any bits of dry mortar.

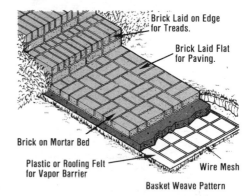

Brick Laid on Edge for Treads.
Brick Laid Flat for Paving.
Brick on Mortar Bed
Plastic or Roofing Felt for Vapor Barrier
Wire Mesh
Basket Weave Pattern

The brick steps in this example were laid in the traditional running bond pattern. Another popular choice is the basket weave pattern, with the bricks either laid flat or on edge as shown in the illustrations.

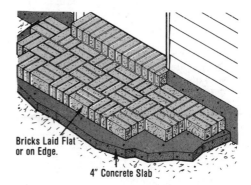

Bricks Laid Flat or on Edge.
4″ Concrete Slab

Tree Wells

Trees can be severely damaged when a site is regraded. Roots might be exposed when the ground level is lowered, and raising a site more than 8″ can cut off needed light, air, and water. In either case, the tree could die.

The solution is to build a tree well, maintaining a circle of ground next to the tree at the level existing before regrading. Not only will a tree well help the tree, it will also make your yard more attractive.

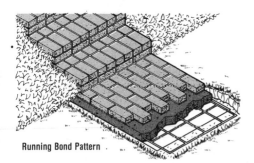

Running Bond Pattern

RAISED TREE WELLS

Physically, a tree well is nothing more than a retaining wall. When the ground is cut away, a raised well keeps the surrounding soil at its original level. Stone, brick, or block can be used, or a concrete wall can be poured. The brick well below is effective, attractive, and easy to build.

Tools and Materials

QUIKRETE® Concrete Mix
QUIKRETE® Mortar Mix or Mason Mix
Brick
Plywood template
Brick trowel, brick hammer, brick set, mason's rule, 4´ level, convex and flat jointers, brush, and screed
Mixing box, mortarboard, wheelbarrow, shovel, and masonry hoe

---

SITE PREPARATION

1. After determining the well size, lay a length of garden hose or rope around the tree where the interior edge of the well will be. Slide a piece of plywood under the hose and mark the arc of the circle on the wood.

2. Cut a 2'- to 3'-long template for the well out of the plywood. The arc will mark the front edge of the template.

3. Excavate a 16"-wide trench, beginning about 4" inside the hose. Dig the trench to several inches below the frost line, keeping the bottom 6" of the trench as smooth as possible so that a footer can be poured without constructing forms.

4. Using the prepared concrete mix, pour a 6" footer. Screed it smooth, and level. Cure it for at least 1 day.

BUILDING THE WELL

1. Dry-lay 2 wythes of brick around the footer, keeping 1/2" joints between the wythes and bricks. The wythes are laid in a horizontal running bond so that head joints do not extend through the width of the wall. Mark the location of the bricks on the footer.

2. Remove the bricks and lay a 1/2" bed of the prepared mortar mix on the footer. Prepare only as much mortar as can be used in an hour.

3. Lay the first course in the mortar bed—do not butter the head joints or the joints between the wythes. These are left open so moisture can escape and to prevent cracks in the wall. Plumb and level each brick, using the template to keep the well plumb from point to point.

4. Using 1/2" bed joints and a vertical running bond in each wythe, build up the well to the former ground level. Plumb and level as you go.

5. After each course is laid, clean out any mortar that falls into the head joints. Use metal ties to bond the wythes together every 5 to 6 courses.

6. Tool the joints with the convex jointer as they are setting up. After the joints harden, brush out any loose mortar.

7. Lay the top course with headers, buttering both sides of the bricks before laying them. Tool the top joints flat to prevent moisture entry.

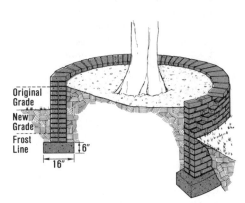

SUNKEN TREE WELL

To keep the tree's root system close to necessary nutrients when the ground level is raised, a sunken tree well is constructed. Site preparation is the same as described earlier; well construction can also be done according to the method already described, except that for a sunken tree well, *all* joints are mortared, and the exterior face of the well is parged with cement up to the grade line.

A simple alternative to brick construction, which can be used for either raised or sunken wells, is mortarless block construction with QUIKWALL® Surface Bonding Cement. (See page 104.)

Concrete Block Construction

Use QUIKRETE® Mortar Mix or Mason Mix to lay up a concrete block wall as shown.

Tools and Materials

QUIKRETE® Mortar Mix or Mason Mix
Concrete block
Mason's line, line blocks, 4´ level, brick trowel, jointer, mason's hammer, and stiff brush
Mixing board, hoe, and mortarboard

LAYING THE FIRST COURSE

1. Excavate the site and construct the footing.

2. Locate the corners of the wall on the footing. Dry-lay the first course of blocks, leaving space for the mortar. Snap a chalk line to mark the position of the blocks on the footing.

3. Pick up the blocks and spread a full bed of QUIKRETE® Mortar Mix or Mason Mix on the footing. Use a trowel to furrow the mortar. It is important to have plenty of mortar along the bottom edges of the block for the first course.

4. Position the corner block carefully, with the thicker end of the face shell up; all blocks should be laid this way to provide a larger mortar bedding

area. When handling a block, always tip it slightly toward you so that you can see the edge of the course below.

5. Place several blocks on end and apply mortar to their vertical face shells. Push each block down into the mortar bed and against the previously laid block. Joints should be about 3/8" thick.

6. After three or four blocks have been laid, use a level to check for plumbness and correct alignment. Make any adjustments by tapping the block with the trowel handle, then complete the first course. Make *all* adjustments while the mortar is still soft. Any attempt to move a block after the mortar has stiffened will break the bond, weakening the wall and allowing moisture to penetrate.

LAYING THE REMAINING COURSES

1. With the remaining courses, mortar is applied to the horizontal face shells of each block; for the vertical joints, mortar either the previously laid block or the block to be placed, but not both. As each block is laid, cut off the excess mortar with the trowel.

2. When laying the remainder of the wall, the corners should be built first, usual-

ly 4 or 5 courses at a time. As each course is laid at the corner, it should be stepped back a half block. Check for plumbness, alignment, and horizontal spacing of the blocks.

3. To fill in the wall between corners, stretch a mason's line from corner to corner and lay the top outside edge of the blocks against it. When placing the closure block, all edges of the opening and all four vertical edges of the closure block should be buttered with mortar. Make sure all joints are tight and weatherproof.

4. Work the joints after each section of the wall has been laid, and the mortar has partially hardened. Proper tooling produces uniform joints with sharp, clean lines. Tool the horizontal joints first, then work the vertical joints with an S-shaped jointer.

5. Wood plates can be fastened to the top course. Use 1/2"-diameter, 18"-long anchor bolts in the cores of the top 2 courses, no more than 4' apart. Fill the cores with mortar, making sure that the bolts extend a few inches above the top of the wall.

For Best Results

Use QUIKRETE® Masonry Coating to waterproof both above and below the grade line.

DECORATIVE BLOCK SCREEN WALLS

Walls, fences, and partitions constructed of concrete masonry screen block offer privacy and provide partial sun and wind control. Since most decorative block is laid up using continuous vertical mortar joints that are weaker than the staggered joints used in standard block and brick work, your main concern when planning and constructing a screen wall project will be stability and strength.

Fortunately, in most home and garden applications, screen walls are required to bear no more than their own weight. In fact, many building codes prohibit the use of screen block in load-bearing applications. Nonload-bearing screen walls require varying amounts of vertical and horizontal support based on wall height, length, block thickness and design, and local weather conditions. Check your local building codes before beginning a screen block project of appreciable size.

Low decorative walls up to a height of 3' or so usually only require welded steel joint reinforcement in the bed joints of every other course. Screen walls higher than 3' generally require additional lateral support provided by reinforced concrete block pilasters or vertical steel channels built into the wall at properly spaced intervals. Steel channel must be either fully grouted or tied into the adjacent block with suitable metal ties.

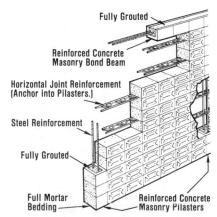

Fully Grouted

Reinforced Concrete Masonry Bond Beam

Horizontal Joint Reinforcement (Anchor into Pilasters.)

Steel Reinforcement

Fully Grouted

Full Mortar Bedding

Reinforced Concrete Masonry Pilasters

Tools and Materials

QUIKRETE® Mortar Mix or Mason Mix
Decorative concrete block
Welded steel joint reinforcement
Steel channel and metal ties (if needed)
Mixing board, hoe, and hawk
Mason's line, line block, 4′ level, brick trowel, jointer, and stiff brush

LAYING THE SCREEN WALL

1. Construct a footing one block length longer than the wall. (Refer to page 4.)

2. Drive a stake into the ground at the end of the footer opposite the end where wall construction will begin. The leading edge of the stake is placed on the front line of the wall, with a nail driven into it at the exact height of the first course.

3. Set the opposite end block in place. Using a line block, attach a mason's line from the end block to the nail in the stake. Dry-lay the first course of blocks along the line, leaving 1/2″ joints between the blocks. Mark the location of the blocks on the footer.

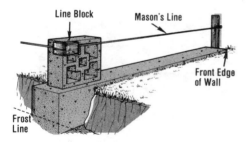

4. Lay a 1/2″ bed of the prepared mortar mix along the footer and lay the first course from the end opposite the stake. By laying the course from end to end, rather than building the corners first, the first course can be off an inch or two without having to cut a closure block.

5. Butter the ends of each block before setting it in place, making certain to set the blocks level.

6. The remaining courses are laid similarly to the first course, using the vertical joints in the bottom course as guides. Butter the ends and bottom of blocks in the upper courses before placing them. Use the level to check alignment every 3 to 4 blocks and to check plumb every 2 to 3 courses.

7. Place the welded steel joint reinforcement in the bed joints of every other course. Stop the reinforcement short of the ends of the wall.

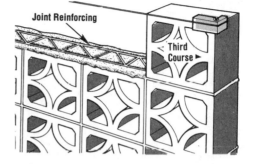

8. Press the reinforcement into the mortar bed prior to placing the lead block of the course. Trowel additional mortar onto the reinforcement and lift it slightly as you set each block in position. This helps embed the steel at the midpont of the joint. Be careful to maintain a consistent joint thickness.

9. Strike the joints after the mortar begins to harden; use a stiff-bristled brush to remove any loose particles of mortar.

10. Moist-cure the mortar for 3 to 4 days by misting the wall with a fine spray several times daily.

For Best Results

Mineral pigments can be added to the mortar mix to match the color of the block. QUIKRETE® liquid Cement Color may also be used. For more information on colored finishes, refer to page 36.

When hollow masonry units are laid with their cores vertical, the top course should be capped to prevent the entrance of water into the wall interior.

Stone Masonry: Planters and Walls

Low maintenance requirements and indefinite durability make stone masonry as financially appealing as it is visually attractive. There are two principal styles. Ashlar, or cut stone, creates a formal effect and is frequently used in the construction of commercial and similar buildings. Rubblestone construction has a more rustic appearance because the stone is either not cut at all or receives only a rough cut. Either style can be laid in courses or at random, with or without mortar. However, ashlar is easier to work with because the shapes are more even. For the same reason, ashlar is also much more expensive than rubblestone. An ashlar project of almost any size requires that the stone be purchased rather than cut by you, while rubblestone may be laid up just as you find it, free in the fields.

In addition to the projects that follow, consider building such things as tree wells, barbecue pits, and fireplaces from stone. Even structural walls can take advantage of stone's endurance and beauty with careful construction techniques. Stone is heavy so work carefully to avoid pinching fingers and toes. Wear work gloves if the stone is particularly rough, and always wear safety goggles or glasses when cutting or breaking up stone with a chisel or sledgehammer.

ASHLAR PLANTER (MORTARED)

Tools and Materials

QUIKRETE® Concrete Mix, and QUIK-RETE® Mortar Mix or Mason Mix

2 x 4 or 2 x 8 scrap lumber, nails, and claw or ball peen hammer

Stone (1 ton = approximately 50 to 60 square feet, 6″ thick)

Mason's hammer, 2lb. mash hammer, plain stone chisel, 2′ level, 2′ square, mason's modular rule, 50′ steel tape, slicker jointer, pointing trowel, ball of line, line pins, and brush

Mixing box, shovel, hoe, mortarboard, wheelbarrow, bucket, and hose

FOOTER CONSTRUCTION

1. Stake out an area for a footer 4″ to 5″ beyond the planter edge on all sides. Excavate deep enough to allow an 8″ to 10″ footer to be sunk below the frost line.

2. Pour the footer with QUIKRETE® Concrete Mix (see page 11). Earth or wood forms can be used.

3. If the planter is to be built on a slope, step the footer as shown in order to save on concrete.

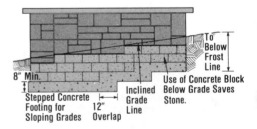

8″ Min.

Stepped Concrete Footing for Sloping Grades

12″ Overlap

Inclined Grade Line

To Below Frost Line

Use of Concrete Block Below Grade Saves Stone.

4. Depending on how far below grade the footer must be sunk in order to be beneath the frost line, stone can be saved by using concrete blocks to bring the foundation up to the grade level as shown in the diagram. Fill the hollows in the blocks with stone chips and mortar to make a firm base for laying the stone.

PLANTER CONSTRUCTION

1. Cure the footer for 3 to 4 days before building the planter. Drive stakes and run a mason's line between them parallel to the footer to keep the planter in alignment.

2. The planter is laid up by working from the ends toward the middle.

Dry-lay the stones first to obtain proper placement; remember to leave 1/2″ head joints between stones.

3. Prepare the QUIKRETE® Mortar Mix or Mason Mix and lay a 1/2″ mortar bed along the footer. You are now ready to begin building the planter.

7. Rake out the joints to a depth of 1/2″ after the mortar has set slightly; this will highlight the stone edges. If a slicker jointer is not available for this, use a wooden dowel or small stick.

4. Butter the head joints of the stones before setting them in place. Once the first course has been laid, spread a layer of mortar on top of the stones and begin laying the second course.

8. After the second course has been laid, it will probably be necessary to raise the mason's line in order to check that the planter is straight. Because the face of stone is not smooth like brick, the stone is plumbed "bump to bump."

5. For stability, use larger stones to tie the wall together at the corners.

9. Continue building the planter to the desired height, using larger end stones on each additional course. Generally, ashlar planters are constructed 5 or 6 courses high.

6. Use the trowel to pack mortar in the joints between courses.

10. When the mortar is dry enough not to smear, brush out all of the joints.

For Best Results

Check local requirements before beginning the project. Many municipalities require a building permit and engineer's approval for any structure more than 3' high.

To make the foundation more secure, lay parallel 3/8" reinforcing rods lengthwise in the footer and install a 3" gravel drainage bed against it.

Clean bedding faces of the stones of all dirt, soil, and vegetable matter before they are laid so that a strong mortar bond is made.

Use small wooden wedges beneath large stones; their weight might squeeze the mortar out of the joints. After the mortar stiffens, remove the wedges and pack the holes with mortar or QUIKRETE® Quick-Setting Cement.

If lighting fixtures are to be mounted on the planter, lay the conduit in the wythe cavity at the desired height as work progresses.

RUBBLESTONE WALLS

Tools and Materials

QUIKRETE® Concrete Mix, and QUIK-RETE® Mortar Mix or Mason Mix
2 x 4 or 2 x 8 scrap lumber, nails, and claw or ball peen hammer
Stone
Stone sledgehammer, 2lb. mash hammer, bricklayer's trowel, pointing trowel, slicker jointer, 50' steel tape, 4' level, ball of line, brush, batter board, plain stone chisel, pointing chisel, and rolling bead jointer (if desired)
Mixing box, shovel, hoe, wheelbarrow, and mortarboard

Rubblestone construction will blend a wall naturally with a surrounding lawn or landscape. Care in selecting and laying the stones must be taken if you are going to use a coursed pattern.

BASE CONSTRUCTION

1. Follow steps 1 through 4 in the preceding section.

2. The wall is constructed after the footer has cured for 3 to 4 days. Begin by laying a large stone, approximately as wide as the wall, at each end of the footer. The mortar bed should be thick enough so that the stone rests completely in it, but should not be deeper than 2".

3. String a line between stakes placed at the wall line on each end of the footer. The face of each stone should be no more than 1" from the string.

4. Lay the first course in two wythes within the guides, keeping the bed and head joints no more than 2" thick. Use care in selecting the stones so that a larger joint is not required. Larger stones should be used at the bottom of the wall for stability. They will also be easier to position there.

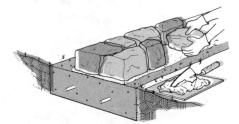

5. On wider walls and where stones cannot be fitted without leaving a gap of 2" or less, use stone chips and mortar to fill cavities.

6. Stones of approximate wall-width are laid across the wall at intervals. Bondstones, as they are called, should be placed so that there is one for every 6 to 10 square feet of wall surface to tie the wall together.

BUILDING THE WALL

1. Both wythes are worked simultaneously in building up the wall to its full height, with larger stones at lower levels and smaller stones toward the top. Slope the wall inward on both sides 1" for each foot of vertical rise. Use a batter board, which can be built out of scrap wood, to keep the wall plumb.

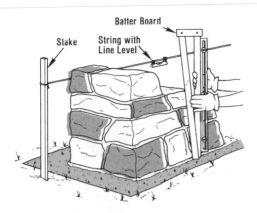

2. Lay end stones first and work toward the middle of the wall. Dry-lay the stones first to obtain proper placement before laying down the mortar. Head joints between stones are not buttered as with brick. Instead, after the stone is set in the mortar bed, mortar is slushed into the head joints between the stones.

3. Periodically lay two smaller stones against a larger one (called a *two against one*) as each course is laid out. Also, periodically overlap stones. In addition to creating a more natural look, these methods create a firmer bond within the wall.

4. As each course is laid, fill in the cavity between wythes before proceeding to the next course. Bondstones should be set in each course.

5. Broad, thinner stones are laid on top as capping. If possible, they should project 1″ on all sides as a drip edge. Tool the joints concave to reduce moisture from entering.

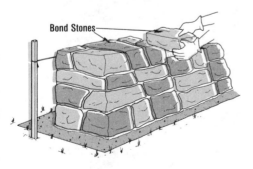

FINISHING THE JOINTS

1. Rake out the wall joints 1/2″ to 3/4″ thick after the mortar has achieved a slight set. Smooth the joints flat with the slicker jointer (use pointing trowel

for broader joints) to highlight the stone edges.

2. Brush any loose mortar particles from the joints after they are hard enough to be brushed without smearing.

3. As an alternative, a rolling bead joint can be applied to the wall. After the joints have been raked out to 3/4″ and brushed, moisten an area that can be pointed within 15 minutes. **DO NOT** soak the joint.

4. Apply fresh mortar to the joint with a rolling bead jointer, which can be purchased or made from a section of 3/4″ copper pipe. Apply with a smooth, steady motion from the leading edge of the joint.

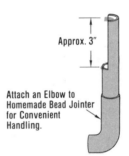

5. Blend the joints as smoothly as possible at intersections so that the joints appear unbroken. Going over a joint already laid might pull it away onto the jointer.

6. Brush joints lightly with a soft brush after they have hardened.

For Best Results

Clean all faces of stone before laying them. Dirt, soil, and vegetable matter will prevent the mortar and stone from bonding.

Check local ordinances. Many municipalities require a building permit and an engineer's approval before a wall higher than 3′ can be built.

Construct a small section of the wall to use as a rough gauge of how much mortar to mix and how much will be needed for building the rest of the wall.

The weight of large stones can squeeze mortar out of their bedding joints. Insert small wooden wedges under the stones when they are laid. After the mortar has set enough to hold the weight, remove the wedges and pack the holes with mortar or QUIKRETE® Quick-Setting Cement.

If stones are in short supply, use concrete blocks to bring the foundation up to the front grade level.

Be sure to keep your tools slightly damp while pointing in order to ease the work. Wipe excess mortar off the tools after each application.

Brick, Block, and Stone Retaining Walls

As with the concrete retaining walls discussed on page 16, brick, block, and stone retaining walls protect your property from soil erosion while, at the same time, adding distinction to your home's exterior. The building procedures are the same as those used in basic wall construction; refer to the *Footers, Basic Brick Construction, Concrete Block Construction,* and *Stone Masonry* sections for details. The tools and materials needed are also identical to those necessary for basic wall construction, with the following additions: 1" plastic pipe (for drainage); QUIKRETE® Masonry Coating (for coating the brick and block walls); and a screen (for covering the pipe on the stone wall).

BUILDING THE WALLS

1. Before beginning work on any retaining wall, check local ordinances and building codes. Many municipalities require a building permit and an engineer's approval before a wall higher than 3' can be built.

2. For added structural integrity in the brick retaining wall, insert steel rebars between the wythes as shown in the illustration. Pour a wet mixture of

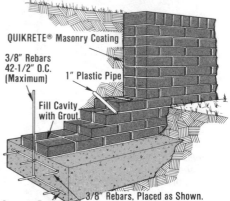

QUIKRETE® Masonry Coating

3/8" Rebars 42-1/2" O.C. (Maximum)

1" Plastic Pipe

Fill Cavity with Grout

3/8" Rebars, Placed as Shown. Minimum 3" from Outside of Concrete.

Concrete Footing 24" Wide x 14" Deep

QUIKRETE® Mortar Mix or Mason Mix between the wythes to bond the rebars. On the concrete block wall, use rebars in the block cavities for horizontal reinforcement. Additional reinforcement is not necessary on the stone wall because it is built lower to the ground than the other walls.

3. Because weep holes are essential for proper drainage, a length of plastic pipe must be installed approximately every 6' along the retaining walls.

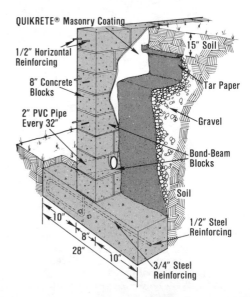

QUIKRETE® Masonry Coating

15" Soil

1/2" Horizontal Reinforcing

8" Concrete Blocks

Tar Paper

2" PVC Pipe Every 32"

Gravel

Bond-Beam Blocks

Soil

10"

1/2" Steel Reinforcing

8"

28"

10"

3/4" Steel Reinforcing

Notch the brick/block to accommodate the pipes and use mortar to secure them as shown in the illustrations. On the stone walls, slope the pipe downward toward the front of the wall, about 8″ above the front grade; this will help prevent pressure buildup against the back of the wall. Place a screen over the back opening and pile broken stone over the screen to prevent the pipe from becoming clogged.

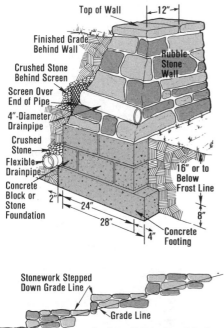

4. Brush a coat of QUIKRETE® Masonry Coating on the back of the finished brick and block walls to make them watertight.

Brick and Stone Veneer Walls

Veneer masonry is a popular choice for home building and remodeling, because it gives the appearance of a solid brick or stone wall while providing better economy and insulation. It can be used as an addition to conventional wood frame structures, and can also be placed on concrete block walls. Depending on personal preference, it may cover an entire wall from foundation to roof, or it can stop at windowsill level.

Tools and Materials

QUIKRETE® Mortar Mix or Mason Mix
Bricks or stones, gravel or crushed stone, reinforcing rebar, forming lumber and stakes (optional, needed only if making new forms), flashing, sheathing, galvanized metal wall ties, masonry nails or stud gun, rubber hose, and story pole
Steel angle (optional), pickax, square-faced shovel, trowel, tamper, saw, wooden wedges, screed, and level

PREPARING THE FOUNDATION

If the footing of the house extends out 6″ or more, the veneer can rest directly on top of it. If the footing is less than 6″,

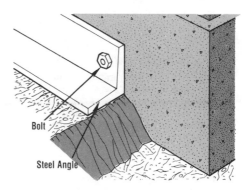

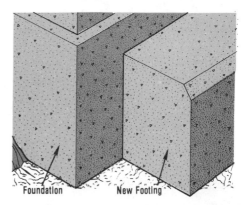

it must be "extended" before the veneer can be placed on it. To "extend" the footing, either bolt a corrosion-resistant steel angle to the existing foundation, or pour a new footing next to the foundation. (See page 11 for footer construction details.) If you are making a new footing, pour a few inches above ground level, then start the veneer at that point. The veneer must always be tied to the old foundation; to ensure a good bond, wash the old foundation surface, and coat it with QUIKRETE® Mortar Mix or Mason Mix.

LAYING A BRICK VENEER WALL

1. Install flashing over the footing to prevent water from seeping behind the veneer. Copper, aluminum, lead, or roofing paper may be used for this. Spread a 1/2" bed of mortar on top of the footing, then push the flashing down firmly into it. (It is a good idea to install flashing at the heads and sills of doors and windows as well.)

2. Cover the existing siding with a good sheathing material, such as tarpaper. Always leave a 1" air space between the sheathing and the veneer.

3. To lay the first course of bricks, use a trowel to spread a 1"-thick bed of mortar on top of the flashing. Tap each brick into place with the trowel handle; never pull on a brick, because this can break the bond. Make sure that all the bricks are plumb and level.

4. To hold the veneer in place, nail galvanized metal wall ties through the siding and into the studs. Space the ties every 32" horizontally and every 16" vertically, and offset the rows so that the ties do not line up.

5. Make weep holes, approximately 24" on center, in the vertical joints of the first course of bricks. To form the weep holes, use short lengths of rubber hose, which can be easily removed after the mortar has set. The weep holes will act as a drainage system to allow any water that may seep in around the flashing to escape.

6. Continue laying each course of bricks, being careful to maintain the precise mortar joint thickness needed to obtain the desired wall height. A story pole may be helpful for accuracy.

7. When you reach a windowsill, lay the bricks on edge in "rowlock" fashion as shown in the illustration. The bricks should also be installed on a slant in the direction of the rainfall. For bricks being laid above windows and doors, a steel lintel must be used as a base. The lintel is set onto the course, even with the head of the window or door; it must overlap the bricks by 3" to 4" on both sides of the window or door.

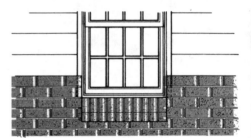

8. If the veneer is being carried all the way to the roof, it must meet the cornice. The frieze board on the cornice should overlap the top course of

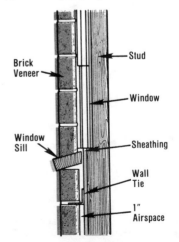

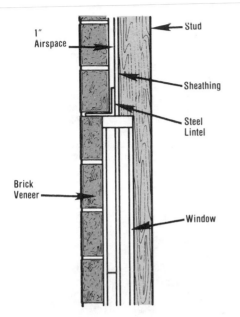

- 1" Airspace
- Stud
- Sheathing
- Steel Lintel
- Brick Veneer
- Window

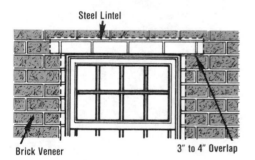

- Steel Lintel
- Brick Veneer
- 3" to 4" Overlap

bricks by at least 1/2". Use 2 × 4 blocking to provide a sound nailing surface for the frieze board.

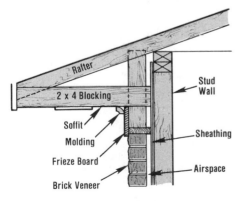

- Rafter
- 2 x 4 Blocking
- Soffit
- Molding
- Frieze Board
- Brick Veneer
- Stud Wall
- Sheathing
- Airspace

LAYING A STONE VENEER WALL

When laying stone veneer on a concrete block wall, the procedure is very similar to the laying of a brick veneer wall:

1. With masonry nails or a stud gun, attach wall ties to the wall every 2 or 3 square feet. (If the concrete block wall is being built from scratch, insert the ties in the mortar joints between the blocks.)

2. Attach the stones to each other and to the wall with mortar. Lay a 1" mortar bed on the footer, and then begin setting the first course of stones; unless you are using a high grade of dressed stone, you will also be setting small stones or gravel in mortar to fill the irregular, open spaces where the large stones do not meet. For each new course, build up a mortar bed and set the stones in place, checking the alignment as you go. Bend as many of the ties as possible into the joints between the stones.

3. Because very large stones can squeeze out all the mortar in their joints, support them temporarily with wooden wedges. When the mortar has set, pull out the wedges and fill the holes with mortar.

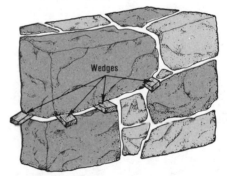

- Wedges

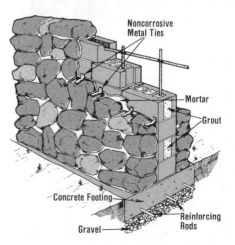

- Noncorrosive Metal Ties
- Mortar
- Grout
- Concrete Footing
- Gravel
- Reinforcing Rods

4. When a section has been laid, use a piece of wood to rake out the joints to a depth of 1/2″ to 3/4″. This will enhance the play of light and shadow on the face of the wall.

Barbecues

A barbecue is a useful and attractive addition to any backyard, whether it's contemporary styled brick or concrete block. It should be located, whenever possible, in a corner of a patio to ensure a solid base.

BRICK BARBECUE

Tools and Materials

QUIKRETE® Fiber-Reinforced Concrete Mix
QUIKRETE® Mortar Mix or Mason Mix
Trowel, hammer, brick set, and float
Mason's line, hand level, chalk, and brush

1. Measure and stake off the desired area. The footer should be 4′ 8″ square and 6″ deep.

2. Prepare the QUIKRETE® Fiber-Reinforced Concrete Mix and place the footer. Using QUIKRETE® Fiber-Reinforced Concrete eliminates the need for rebar in slab-on-grade applications.

3. Draw an outline of the barbecue on the footer, leaving at least 2″ all around. Dry-lay the first two courses to make sure your pattern works; remember to leave 1/2″ mortar joints between bricks.

4. Prepare the QUIKRETE® Mortar Mix or Mason Mix and begin building the barbeque at the corners, making sure to bond the first course to the footer with mortar. Build up four courses high, then fill in from corner to corner.

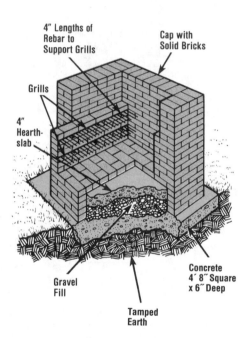

4″ Lengths of Rebar to Support Grills

Cap with Solid Bricks

Grills

4″ Hearthslab

Gravel Fill

Tamped Earth

Concrete 4′ 8″ Square x 6″ Deep

5. Spread a thin layer of loose gravel inside the bricks, then pour a 4″ thick hearthslab using QUIKRETE® Fiber-Reinforced Concrete Mix.

6. Use a hand level to keep the wall plumb and the rows of brick level. Excess mortar can be chipped off with the trowel two or three rows at a time.

7. As construction proceeds, insert 4″ lengths of rebar in the fresh mortar joints to support the grills as shown.

8. Top off the walls of the barbecue with solid bricks.

9. Remove any leftover crumbs of mortar from the barbecue by brushing them away with a soft fiber hand brush.

CONCRETE BLOCK BARBECUE

For an attractive and economical backyard barbecue that is quick and easy to build, yet as sturdy as they come, consider the following one made with concrete blocks and QUIKWALL® Surface Bonding Cement. Or, modify the design to suit your fancy and needs. With the time saved by using QUIKWALL® SBC instead of mortar, you will have plenty of opportunity to exercise your architectural creativity.

Tools and Materials

QUIKRETE® Concrete Mix
QUIKWALL® Surface Bonding
  Cement (SBC)
Concrete block
Steel plate, grill, steel hangers, and
  counterboard
Plasterer's trowel, float, screed, shovel,
hoe, mixing box, hawk, and level

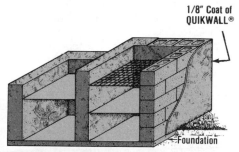

1/8" Coat of QUIKWALL®

Foundation

CONSTRUCTION

1. Excavate an area 24" wider and 8" deeper than the length and combined widths of the grill and counterboard you will use. Dig to a depth of about 4", keeping the edges as straight as possible.

2. Place the prepared concrete mix in the excavation as a footer. Screed and float. Damp-cure the concrete for 3 to 4 days. (For further information on footers and finishing concrete, refer to pages 11 and 32.)

3. Dry-lay the first course of blocks on the footer to determine their correct placement. Begin at one end, interlocking the sidewalls with the back wall. Mark the location of the blocks on the footer.

4. Lay a 1/2" bed of QUIKWALL® SBC on the footer and set the first course in it, beginning at the same end and butting the blocks together. Make certain that this course is set straight and level.

5. Stack the remaining block in a running bond pattern, interlocking all the walls together. Stack the grill walls 5 courses high, and the counter walls 4 courses high, making certain to place them plumb on the course below.

6. Place the steel hangers in the grill sidewalls after the second, third, and fourth courses; place them in the counter sidewalls after the third course.

7. Mix as much QUIKWALL® SBC as can be used in about an hour. Dampen both sides of the block. Trowel apply a minimum 1/8"-thick coat to completely cover the wall surfaces. After 8 hours, mist the barbecue with a fine spray. Repeat this several times daily for 2 to 3 days to moist-cure.

8. Set the counterboard, steel plate, and grill in place on the hangers.

Garden Pools and Fountains

The tranquil beauty and playful shimmer of a reflecting pool or fountain is just the thing to enhance the charm of your garden or patio. Best of all, you can do all the work yourself. Add goldfish or water plants to increase the pool's appeal; fish will even help control the insect population.

FREE-FORM CONCRETE POOL

This pool can be given the dimensions and shape you desire, and all you need to build it is simple construction know-how and a few tools.

Tools and Materials

QUIKRETE® Fiber-Reinforced
  Concrete Mix
QUIKRETE® Acrylic Concrete
  Cure & Seal
QUIKRETE® Mortar Mix or Mason Mix
QUIKRETE® Masonry Coating
Sand
Chicken-wire reinforcement
1"x 2" scrap wood
2" drainpipe and fittings
Shovel, hoe, mixing box, hammer,
  wooden float or trowel, and brush

CONSTRUCTION

1. Dig a saucer-shaped excavation for the pool with a center 24″ deep.

2. Install the drainpipe at the center of the pool as shown. The coupling should be 6″ above the soil bed. The pipe end is connected to a drain or led away to a dry well.

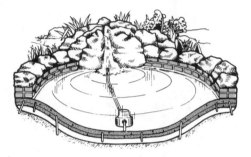

3. Cut the 1 x 2s into 11″ stakes, marking each at 2″, 5″, and 8″ distances from the head. Drive them into the bed at square-foot intervals up to the 8″ mark.

4. Fill the pool with 3″ of sand or gravel as a subbase (up to the 5″ marks).

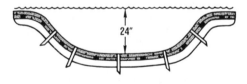

24″

5. Lay the chicken wire into the pool, supporting it about 2″ above the subbase with small stones or brick bits.

6. Pack the prepared QUIKRETE® Fiber-Reinforced Concrete Mix firmly around the chicken wire with the shovel up to

the 2″ stake marks. This will give you a 3″ concrete basin.

7. After the concrete loses its sheen, finish it with a trowel or wooden float.

8. Apply QUIKRETE® Acrylic Concrete Cure & Seal. Fill with water after 1 day.

9. The perimeter of the pool can be built up using QUIKRETE® Mortar Mix or Mason Mix and brick; mortared or dry-laid stone can also be used. The addition of plants and shrubs creates a cool, shaded effect. Painting the bottom green or dark blue will make the pool appear deeper.

10. You may wish to install a submersible, circulating pump to create a tiered waterfall or spray fountain effect in the pool; if so, follow the manufacturer's directions carefully. Naturally, running water produces noise, so you may want to limit the drop of the water or its volume. Be sure to know what type of pump setup you are going to use before building the pool's perimeter. Tubing or electrical cable will likely have to pass through or be concealed by these items.

11. Thoroughly clean and flush the surface of the pool before stocking it with fish or plants.

For Best Results

Vary the depth of the pool to suit your taste, but it should have a minimum center depth of 14″ to keep fish safe from other animals and a 16″ depth for water plants.

A gentle slope makes laying the concrete easier; however, you can make the slopes as steep as you wish. For a steeper slope, mix the concrete with slightly less water than in other construction for convenience in laying it.

For added effect, brush a coat of QUIKRETE® Masonry Coating on the basin. It's available in white, gray, and other popular colors.

CONCRETE BLOCK POOL

An uncomplicated design, the concrete block pool has rectangular corners that add a dignified elegance to any garden, and its construction makes it an easy and economical project to do yourself.

Tools and Materials

QUIKRETE® Concrete Mix
QUIKWALL® Surface Bonding
  Cement (SBC)
QUIKRETE® Masonry Coating
QUIKRETE® Hydraulic Water-Stop
  Cement
QUIKRETE® Concrete Acrylic Fortifier
QUIKRETE® Acrylic Concrete
  Cure & Seal
QUIKRETE® Marble Chips or Deco
  Pebbles
6″ x 8″ x 16″ concrete blocks
2″ x 8″ x 16″ concrete capping blocks
8″ length of 1/2″ copper or plastic
  tubing
Reinforcing wire
1″ x 2″ scrap lumber
Shovel, mason's hammer, trowel, 4′
  level, ball of line, screed, wooden
  float, portable mixer, and brush

SITE EXCAVATION

1. Plan the size of your pool so that no
   blocks will have to be cut. Since no
   mortar will be used, use the actual
   dimensions of the block, which are 1/8″
   less than the nominal dimensions.

2. Stake out an area 1′ wider on the sides
   and ends than the planned external
   dimensions of the pool.

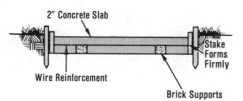

2″ Concrete Slab
Wire Reinforcement
Stake Forms Firmly
Brick Supports

3. Excavate the site. For a reflecting pool
   using only 1 course of blocks, excavate
   at least 4″; for a fish or plant pond using
   2 block courses, excavate at least 12″.
   For the overflow pipe to work, a minimum
   of 3″ of the pool, including the capping
   blocks, must be exposed above ground.

4. The bottom 2″ of the site are excavated
   only to the external dimensions of the
   pool; try to keep these edges straight so
   that the concrete slab can be poured
   without a form.

POOL BASE CONSTRUCTION

1. Lay the reinforcing wire into the pool bed.

2. Pour the prepared concrete around the

wire to a depth of 2″. Use a hook to keep
the wire near the center of the slab for
maximum strength.

3. Screed and float the concrete.

4. If desired, QUIKRETE® Marble Chips or
   QUIKRETE® Deco Pebbles can be
   seeded into the top surface of the wet
   concrete to create an interesting
   exposed aggregate finish for the pool
   bottom. See page 35 for details.

POOL WALL CONSTRUCTION

1. Set the blocks lengthwise into the fresh
   concrete. Lay them outward from a
   corner, butting them together as tightly
   as possible and keeping them aligned
   with the level.

2. Create a watertight seal between the
   base of the pool wall and the pool base
   by forming a cove-shaped joint of
   QUIKWALL® Surface Bonding Cement.

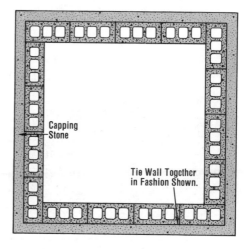

Capping Stone

Tie Wall Together in Fashion Shown.

The batch of QUIKWALL® SBC used to
create the cove must be fortified with
QUIKRETE® Concrete Acrylic Fortifier.
The bottom edge of the cove should
extend out onto the pool base. The top
edge should extend up the wall until it
feathers out.

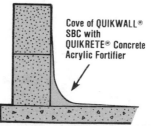

Cove of QUIKWALL®
SBC with
QUIKRETE® Concrete
Acrylic Fortifier

3. The remaining batches of QUIKWALL® SBC do not require QUIKRETE® Concrete Acrylic Fortifier. Trowel the prepared QUIKWALL® SBC on both sides and on the top of the blocks, taking care to completely cover them. One 50-pound bag is sufficient to cover an area of approximately 50 square feet to a depth of 1/8″. The bed on top of the blocks should be a minimum of 1/4″ thick

.4. Lay the capping blocks into the QUIKWALL® SBC bed, overhanging the edges of the wall at least 1″ on all sides. Level the blocks in two directions and make certain they are correctly aligned.

5. Insert the tubing as an overflow pipe under the capping blocks in an appropriate location in your wall. Use QUIKRETE® Hydraulic Water-Stop Cement to seal the opening around the pipe. Do this before laying the capping block.

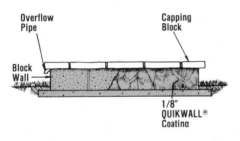

Overflow Pipe
Capping Block
Block Wall
1/8″ QUIKWALL® Coating

6. Apply QUIKRETE® Acrylic Concrete Cure & Seal to the concrete.

For Best Results

A drainpipe can be installed in place of the overflow to drain water at the onset of cold weather.

Sandbox Play Area

Few things exercise a child's imagination like a sandbox, and this project is as easy to build as it is fun to play in. Fill it with QUIKRETE® Play Sand®; it's washed, screened, and rid of all organic matter before being packaged for sale. And don't forget: it's a good idea to have some means of covering the sandbox to keep out rain, leaves, animals, etc.

Tools and Materials

QUIKRETE® Play Sand®
QUIKRETE® All-Purpose Sand
1″ x 4″ edge boards, 1″ x 3″ trim boards, 2″ x 2″ wood and cleats, 5/8″ exterior-grade plywood, tamper, and bricks

1. Stake out and excavate the play area according to the dimensions shown in the illustration. Border the area with 1″ x 4″ edging. For details on excavating and edging, see the *Patios, Walkways, and Driveways* section.

2. If desired, lay a 1″ to 2″ gravel base to improve drainage; this is especially important in damp locales.

3. Use 5/8″ exterior-grade plywood and 2″ x 2″ wood and cleats to construct the sandbox frame according to the dimensions shown in the illustration. Border the frame with 1″ x 3″ trim.

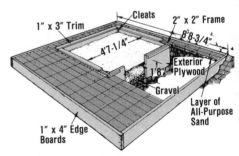

Cleats
2″ x 2″ Frame
1″ x 3″ Trim
8′8-3/4″
4′7-1/4″
1′8″
Exterior Plywood
Gravel
Layer of All-Purpose Sand
1″ x 4″ Edge Boards

4. Fill the sandbox with QUIKRETE® Play Sand®.

5. Spread a 1″ to 2″ layer of QUIKRETE® All-Purpose Sand over the ground surrounding the sandbox. Tamp the surface smooth, then lay the bricks in rowlock fashion over the entire area.

6. Sweep QUIKRETE® All-Purpose Sand into the cracks between the bricks. After removing any excess sand from the surface, wet it down with a very fine spray; be careful not to allow any pools of water to form.

Patios, Walkways, and Stepping Stones:

Using WalkMaker and StepMaker Molds

Building concrete patios and walkways that resemble brick or cobblestone is an easy do-it-yourself project with WalkMaker re-usable plastic molds. WalkMaker molds offer unlimited designs and can be used with a variety of QUIKRETE® Concrete mixes.

Tools and Materials

QUIKRETE® WalkMaker mold– available in Country Stone, Running Bond Brick, and European Block patterns
QUIKRETE® Fiber-Reinforced Concrete or Concrete Mix (Four 60lb. bags or three 80lb. bags will fill three 2´ x 2´ WalkMaker sections)
Mixing equipment (wheelbarrow or mixer), trowel, and shovel

Optional

QUIKRETE® Liquid Cement Color (available in red, brown, buff, charcoal and terra cotta), QUIKRETE® Play Sand, wood chips, pebbles, etc., for color or textures

SITE PREPARATION

Place the WalkMaker mold in the desired location. WalkMaker molds can be placed directly on any relatively flat surface. They will configure the concrete to the existing base. If you prefer, you may remove 1" of top soil and level the WalkMaker mold before filling it with concrete. Removed soil can be used to fill in open spaces alongside concrete after the walk has set up.

MIXING AND PLACEMENT

1. Empty QUIKRETE® Concrete Mix into wheelbarrow and add sufficient water for the amount of concrete being mixed. Mix thoroughly until a plastic-like consistency is achieved. If additional water is required, add small amounts until the proper consistency is obtained.

2. Use a shovel or trowel to fill each mold cavity level to the surface of the mold. Pat and smooth the surface with a trowel.

3. Remove the mold promptly, and smooth the concrete edges with a trowel until the desired appearance is obtained.

4. Place the mold adjacent to the completed section and continue this process until your project is completed. By alternately rotating the WalkMaker mold one quarter turn each time, a variation in the pattern is achieved.

5. If desired, QUIKRETE® Sand Mix or Mortar Mix can be applied dry to the hardened concrete to fill the joints. Brush or sweep the dry mix into the joints and moisten.

6. Cure the concrete properly to develop maximum strength. Moist cure for 5 to 7 days. To protect your finish and eliminate the need for moist curing, use QUIKRETE® Acrylic Concrete Cure & Seal. Cure & Seal insures proper curing and provides a water-resistant coating. It also protects concrete surfaces from the deteriorating effects of grease, oil, salt, and most household chemicals.

ADDING COLOR AND SURFACE TEXTURE

1. Color may be added to any Walk-Maker project with QUIKRETE® Liquid Cement Color. Ten ounces of liquid color should be used for every two 60- or 80-pound bags of any QUIKRETE® Concrete Mix.

2. Mix 1-1/4 gallons of clean water for every 10 ounces of color. When using a mechanical mixer, add both liquids to the mixer and

then add the Concrete Mix. When hand-mixing in a tub or wheelbarrow, mix the color and water, and then add the liquid to the Concrete Mix.

3. Mix thoroughly until the concrete is uniform in color. Add water as needed to achieve a uniform color and workable consistency.

4. A variety of surface textures may be achieved by experimenting with different toppings. This should be done while the concrete is still damp but has reached initial set (approximately 1 hour after concrete has been placed). Some ideas include: small wood chips or pea gravel pressed into the surface of the concrete; irregular trowel imprints; and brushing QUIK-RETE® Play Sand® on the surface.

CORNERS AND CURVES

For corners, simply butt the WalkMaker mold to the last section poured, align in the direction of the turn, and continue.

When making curves, there are two options:

1. Butt outside corner of the mold to the existing concrete, align the curve, and press down on the mold, cutting the freshly placed concrete on the inside corner. Remove the mold and refinish the cut portion of the concrete. Place the mold, fill with concrete, and continue making cuts as necessary to attain the proper curve alignment.

2. Butt inside corner of the mold to the existing concrete. Fill in the space between the mold and the existing concrete on the outside corner. Free form the fill-in space. Level, finish, and shape the fill-in concrete to the desired appearance. Continue the procedure until the curve is complete.

ESTIMATING AMOUNT OF CONCRETE YOU'LL NEED:

From outside edge to outside edge, each WalkMaker is 2′ x 2′; however, the Country Stone pattern interlocks, and the length of walks can be estimated by this chart. (The Running Bond Brick and European Block patterns do not interlock and provide a consistent 2′ x 2′ section.)

Approximate Length of Walk Desired	Country Stone Sections Poured	80lb. bags of Concrete required	60lb.bags of Concrete required
2′	1	1	1-1/3
3′9″	2	2	2-2/3
5′6″	3	3	4
9′	5	5	6-2/3
16′	9	9	12
23′	13	13	17-1/3
30′	17	17	22-2/3

A rule of thumb to follow is each additional poured section of WalkMaker will add 1′9″ to your existing WalkMaker stones. Of course, each WalkMaker is reusable for each section you need to pour, saving money and time over building wooden forms for traditional walks!

StepMaker and BorderMaker Molds

Individual StepMaker and BorderMaker molds can be used to make stepping-stones or garden borders. Stepping-stones are available in round, hexagon, and a four-cobblestone pattern. They can be personalized with a variety of impressions such as hand and leaf prints.

Patios, Walkways, and Driveways:
Brick, Flagstone, Adobe, Stone

Whether the project is a short walkway, a curving drive, or an expansive backyard patio, brick is a surprisingly easy material to work with. Depending on the particular project design, most tools and materials needed can be found in the home. Whatever the project, proper drainage requires a slope of not less than 1″ per 10 lineal feet. The maximum slope for a driveway is 1-3/4″ per foot. Slope away from buildings and toward pavement edges.

SAND BASE

A sand base is an easy method for the beginner and provides good durability in areas not subject to ground-freeze. Two 70-pound bags of QUIKRETE® All-Purpose Sand are enough to cover approximately 144 square feet.

Tools and Materials

QUIKRETE® All-Purpose Sand
Brick Paving
Carpenter's level, mason's line or string, rubber mallet/wooden block, screed, and spade

---

CONSTRUCTING THE PAVEMENT

1. Stake out the site and excavate deep enough to allow a 1″ to 2″ sand bed beneath the brick. For good drainage, the brick surface should be kept 1″ above the grade.

2. Edge the site (see *Edging the Pavement*, page 97).

3. Pour QUIKRETE® All-Purpose Sand to a depth of 1″ to 2″; then wet the sand with a fine spray to settle it. Screed level.

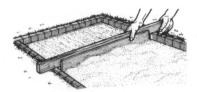

4. Lay bricks outward from a corner, using a mason's line or string to align the rows. Tap and level the bricks in place with a mallet.

5. Sweep QUIKRETE® All-Purpose Sand into the joints; dampen with a fine spray. Resand as needed to fill joints.

For Best Results

Overlay the base with an asphalt-saturated felt or dark polyethylene plastic to prevent weed growth through bricks.

Underlay the base with 1″ to 2″ of gravel or crushed rock to improve drainage in damp locales.

DRY MORTAR

Using dry mortar is almost as easy as using sand and increases the pavement's permanence in areas subject to frost heave. The brick is bonded at the joints, providing a more stable way to construct a driveway.

Tools and Materials

QUIKRETE® Sand Mix
QUIKRETE® All-Purpose Sand
Brick Paving
Level, mason's line, rubber mallet/ wooden block, 1/2″ wood spacer, burlap sack, and spade

CONSTRUCTING THE PAVEMENT

1. Follow steps 1 through 4 as in the sand base method, using a spacer to place the bricks.

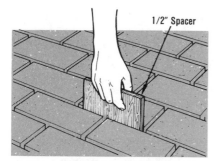

1/2" Spacer

2. Sweep QUIKRETE® Sand Mix into the joints; use a spacer to tamp the mix for firmer bonding.

3. After removing any excess mix from the paving surface, wet it down with a very fine spray, taking care not to allow any pools to form or mix to splash out of the joints.

4. Let set for about 2 hours, then scrub the brick face with a wet burlap sack to remove any spillover.

For Best Results

Before spreading the sand mix, make sure brick is dry to avoid staining.

Spray twice to assure sufficient moisture to bond joints.

For a professional look, smooth the joints with a wooden dowel or broom handle after the mix begins to harden.

For a firmer foundation, use QUIKRETE® Sand Mix for the base instead of sand. No additional spraying is needed.

WET MORTAR

Tools and Materials

QUIKRETE® Mason Mix
QUIKRETE® Sand (Topping) Mix
QUIKRETE® Concrete Acrylic Fortifier
Brick paving and 1 x 4 lumber
Level, mason's line, rubber mallet/
wooden block, 1/2" wood spacer,
small masonry trowel, burlap sack,
flat-edged shovel, and ball peen
hammer

In this method the pavers are set in wet mortar over a 4" to 6" concrete slab. This permanent installation method is needed in areas with severe winters or highly unstable soil. Thoroughly clean the slab removing all dirt, paint, oil or other surface contaminants.

LAYING THE BRICK

1. Construct a header with 1 x 4 lumber against all the open sides of the slab.

2. The wet mortar bed can be made with Mason Mix or a blend of Sand Mix with Acrylic Fortifier added. The latter combination is recommended for the most freeze-thaw durable application. Place the mixed mortar at a depth of 1/2". Only screed 10 sq. ft. at a time.

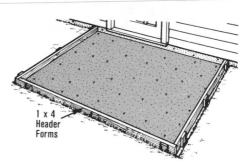

1 x 4
Header
Forms

3. Lay brick outward from a corner, leaving 1/2" joints between the bricks. Use level and line for proper placement, and remember to level in two directions, using mallet/block to place the brick.

4. After letting the brick set in the base for about 4 hours, use a small trowel to carefully work the mortar into the joints. Minimize spillage to avoid staining brick.

5. Let harden 1/2 hour, then finish the joints with a jointer, broom handle, or wooden dowel.

6. Use a wet burlap sack to remove any spillage from brick after about 2 more hours.

For Best Results

To prevent bricks from absorbing too much moisture from the mortar, wet them down several hours before using them.

Mix only enough mortar at one time as you can use in about an hour.

FLAGSTONE, STONE, AND ADOBE

Other paving materials such as flagstone, stone, and adobe can be used instead of brick, depending on the effect desired and the time and expense that can be afforded. Generally, brick is the most versatile for time, design, and economy; but the basic construction techniques and slope requirements are similar for all.

Flagstone is larger and more expensive than brick and is usually laid in an irregular pattern that complements its varying shapes and sizes. It can be cut the same way as brick, if necessary, or it can be purchased precut.

Due to its weight and size, flagstone can be laid directly on an extremely stable, level soil base. In areas where drainage is poor or where traffic is heavy (such as walkways), lay the flagstone on a 3″ or deeper sand base. The dry mortar method can also be used to provide more stability.

For patios and driveways, the wet mortar method is best for setting flagstone. As with all paving, your area's climate will dictate which method is best for any project.

River rock, field stone, and cast concrete pavers are less expensive than flagstone. Sand bed, dry mortar, or wet mortar installation methods can be used. A sand base works well with most concrete paver applications, while the irregular shape and texture of rock and stone make wet mortar the best choice for these materials.

HOMEMADE CONCRETE PAVERS

Precast concrete pavers, often called patio pavers, are available in a wide range of shapes, sizes, and colors. Square, rectangular, or special interlocking designs can be used to create any number of striking patterns. You can also cast concrete pavers using QUIKRETE® Concrete Mix or QUIKRETE® Sand Mix. The simplest method of casting pavers is to dig an earth form in firmly packed soil. Fill the hole with the prepared mix, smooth the surface of the pour, and allow it to cure fully. Reusable wooden forms

Soil Form for Homemade Pavers

are also easy to build and use. For special effect, seed the bottom of the mold with a layer of decorative aggregate before adding the concrete. Pour the concrete slowly so as not to displace the stone. When the concrete cures, the exposed aggregate becomes the top surface of the paver.

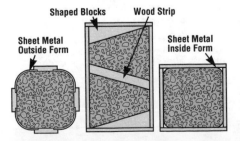

Shaped Blocks   Wood Strip   Sheet Metal Outside Form   Sheet Metal Inside Form

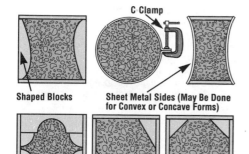

Shaped Blocks

C Clamp

Sheet Metal Sides (May Be Done for Convex or Concave Forms)

Triangular Blocks

PAVING WITH ADOBE

The simple, economical sand base method is the best way to lay adobe paving. Use 1″ joints between pieces to allow for irregular block sizes and provide proper drainage. To prevent cracking of the finished installation, be sure that the sand base is level and free from stone or gravel.

EDGING THE PAVEMENT

Edging is needed to stabilize the pavement and can most often improve its appeal. Three common methods are shown below.

Soldiers. This is the simplest method. A border of bricks set on end is placed between the pavement site and the surrounding soil. The soil must be firm enough to hold the soldiers in place.

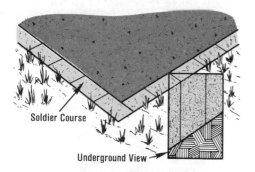

Soldier Course

Underground View

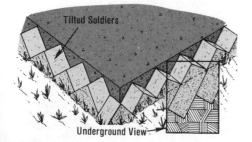

Tilted Soldiers

Underground View

Invisible Edging. As the name indicates, an obvious border can be avoided with this method. It is also more stable than using soldiers. A footer of QUIKRETE® Concrete Mix is poured around the perimeter of the paving site. The footer will be one brick length wide and 2″ deep, with the top set one brick width below ground level. After the footer has set, bricks are laid along it in the same method used for the pavement.

See *Edging* on page 71 for constructing similar brick edging without the use of wooden forms.

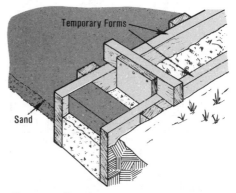

Temporary Forms

Sand

Concrete Edging. This is constructed in the same manner as invisible edging, except that the surface of the footer is brought flush with ground level. The face remains exposed and can be finished in a number of attractive ways or simply left smooth.

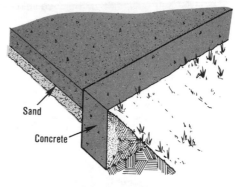

Sand

Concrete

WORKING WITH PAVING MATERIALS

Patterns. The advantage of brick and adobe over stone is that a pattern can be created in the pavement. There are several common methods, or the builder can invent one of his own. The easiest methods for the beginner are those which do not require cutting the paving material. These methods will also reduce waste.

Some common patterns, and whether or not cutting is required, are shown here.

Basket Weave

Stack

Running Stack

Diagonal

Running Bond

Basket Weave Variation

Herringbone

Diagonal Herringbone Jack on Jack Combination

Cutting. Brick, stone, and adobe are cut similarly. A brick set or broad-bladed cold chisel, mason's hammer, and safety glasses are necessary. The brick is set on a flat surface, and the chisel is placed on the cutline with the bevel facing away from the side to be used. A small groove is cut across all four sides with light hammer taps, and a sharp blow on the broad surface will make the final cut. For larger stones, one end is placed on a solid support, and the unsupported end is tapped to make the final cut. The chisel end of the hammer is used to chip away any rough edges.

Laying the Pavement. Whatever material is used, laying begins at a corner and moves outward. Leveling is done in two directions. Except for brick on a sand base, all paving should have at least 1/2″ joints to allow for the mortar fill. Depending on the look desired, the joints should be finished with a trowel or similar object after being filled. To prevent displacing previously laid bricks, a long board should be knelt on while laying the pavement.

Cleaning. Again, depending on the desired effect, you may wish to clean the brick or stone if mortar stains appear. To do this after the mortar has set, soak the area to be cleaned, and then mix a solution of 9 parts water to 1 part muriatic acid. Use rubber gloves to scrub the area, then rinse it thoroughly to prevent acid burns.

Tile Installation

Tile is an extremely versatile surface covering that can be used over floors, ceilings, countertops, hearths, and shower and bath enclosures. Used in combination with QUIKRETE® Thin-Set mixes and grouts, it provides an attractive and durable covering both indoors and out.

Tools and Materials

QUIKRETE® Multi-Purpose Thin-Set (for setting tile on a variety of surfaces, including exterior-grade plywood and other hard-to-bond surfaces)
QUIKRETE® Thin-Set Sanded (for setting tile on concrete, plaster, gypsum wallboard, old tile surfaces, marble, gypsum plaster brown coat, and gypsum block)
QUIKRETE® Polymer-Modified Tile Grouts (for use with both highly absorptive and vitreous tile)
QUIKRETE® Concrete & Asphalt Cleaner (for cleaning cement grout residue buildup from tile surfaces)
QUIKRETE® Acrylic Concrete Cure & Seal (for sealing tile from dirt buildup)
Tiles, spacers, glass cutter, pliers or nippers, notched trowel, chalk line, plumb bob, rubber float or squeegee, towels or cheesecloth, and level

Note: For more information on QUIKRETE® tile-setting products, see pages 162 and 163.

TILING FLOORS

When installing tile over a concrete floor, make sure that the slab is level, properly cured, and free of any dirt, wax, or curing compounds. If it is cracked or damaged in any way, repair it before laying the tile. (See *Repairing Concrete* on page 129 for details.)

When installing tile over wooden sub-flooring, the bonding surface must be exterior-grade plywood. The plywood should bring the finish floor thickness to a minimum of 1″; it must be solid, with minimal deflection. To apply exterior-grade plywood, first glue plywood backing in place, then fasten 5d coated nails 8″ apart in every direction. Leave a 1/8″ space between sheets of plywood to allow for expansion.

For installation over wooden subflooring in wet areas, either cement backer boards or a cement plaster coat reinforced with metal lath must be applied prior to tiling. To apply cement backer board, mix QUIKRETE® Multi-Purpose Thin-Set and apply it to the subflooring. Immediately lay the backer board over the subflooring, allowing a 1/8″ space between boards. Fasten with 1-1/2″ galvanized roof nails every 6″.

When installing tile over a minimum 1″ thick plywood floor that is sound and shows no sign of deflection, first apply minimum 1/4″ exterior-grade plywood. Fasten the plywood as described previously. For installation over vinyl flooring with a concrete base, first remove the vinyl covering. Then use a liquid stripper and scraper to remove all mastic residue.

SETTING FLOOR TILE

The following method is particularly effective for rooms with large doorways that make the floor visible from other parts of the house.

1. Snap a chalk line down the center of the room perpendicular to the doorway. Now snap another chalk line perpendicular to the first.

2. Starting at the doorway, dry-lay tiles along the first chalk line. Use appropriately sized tile spacers between each tile so that the grout spaces will be uniform.

3. If you do not have enough room for a full tile at the end of the line, use a cut tile at each end so that the spaces are equal. To cut a tile, score it with a glass cutter, then lay it over a nail or piece of metal and press down on both sides. Use pliers or nippers to remove any rough edges.

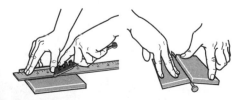

4. Dry-lay tiles along the second chalk line, again using spacers. If necessary, adjust the lines so that they intersect at a tile corner as shown in the illustration.

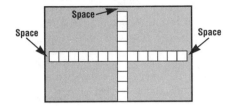

5. Draw a line on the floor to mark the outside edge of the last full tile at the doorway. Make sure the line is straight and extend it along the entire length of the wall. Repeat this procedure on one of the adjacent walls.

6. Place long 1 x 2s or 1 x 3s on the outside of each line. Make sure that they are perfectly square, then nail them in place.

7. Beginning in the corner where the boards intersect, spread approximately 3 square feet of Thin-Set mix with a notched trowel. Hold the trowel at a 45° angle to achieve maximum coverage. Set the corner tile into the mix with a firm, twisting motion.

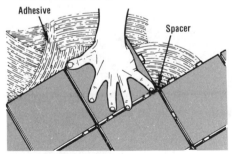

8. Continue setting the tiles according to the order shown in the illustration. Always use spacers between the tiles to keep the alignment straight. Use a rubber mallet to tamp down any uneven tiles and wipe all excess mortar off the surface immediately. When the mortar has set, remove the boards. Lay cut tiles along the edges, leaving an 1/8″ gap along the wall.

9. Remove the spacers and wait at least 48 hours before grouting.

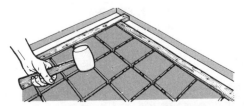

GROUTING

1. Use QUIKRETE® Acrylic Concrete Cure & Seal before grouting over unglazed tile to avoid staining the tile during the application.

2. Mix the QUIKRETE® Polymer-Modified Tile Grout thoroughly to insure color uniformity.

3. Use a hard rubber float to work the grout diagonally across the joints until they are packed full and are flush with the surface. Turn the float perpendicular to the tile, and remove excess grout with a squeegee.

4. When the grout reaches its initial set, clean the tile with a slightly damp towel or cheesecloth. Use a circular rubbing motion.

5. Wait at least 10 days, then clean the new tile with QUIKRETE® Concrete & Asphalt Cleaner.

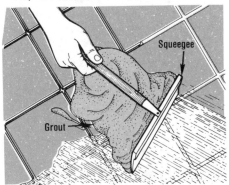

TILING WALLS

If you're tiling over an existing wall, the surface must be free of dirt and wax, and it should be sanded down, if it is glossy. If the wall has extensive cracks and other surface defects, install wallboard or some other new backing material over it. If working over cement, drywall, or plaster, use QUIKRETE® Multi-Purpose Thin-Set. In wet areas, use cement backer board or moisture-resistant gypsum board. Fill all corners and cracks with Multi-Purpose Thin-Set, followed by a surface coat. If working over ceramic wall tile, clean and abrade the surface first, then use Multi-Purpose Thin-Set for the bonding application.

SETTING WALL TILE

This procedure makes use of a layout rod, a special tool that enables you to simulate a dry run for the installation.

1. Find the center point of the wall and snap a plumb line from the ceiling to the floor. Snap two more plumb lines close to the edges of the wall.

2. Snap a horizontal chalk line across the exact center of the wall, then snap two more horizontal lines as close to the floor and ceiling as possible. These six lines will provide the centerlines for beginning the tile installation. They also point out where your walls and floors are uneven; in such cases, the tiles must be tapered so that they will fit snugly against the wall.

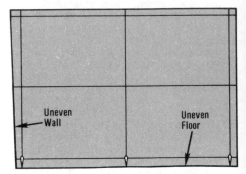

3. To make the layout rods, cut two 1 x 2s to the height and width of the wall. Use a compass to mark a tile layout along each rod, adjusting the grout spacing and location of the cut tiles until you are satisfied. If you are using special tile or trim pieces as a border, be sure to include them on the proper ends of the rods.

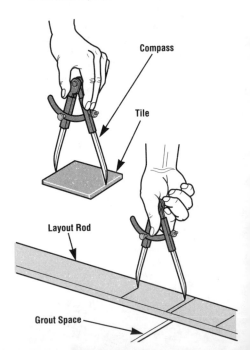

4. To transfer the marks from the rods to the wall, hold each rod against two of the plumb lines or horizontal lines.

5. Begin installing tile on the bottom row, starting at the centerline. Apply enough Multi-Purpose Thin-Set for the first few tiles, but leave the baseline and centerline visible for accurate alignment.

6. Set the first tiles in place, and insert spacers between them. Many wall tiles have nubs on the sides to provide the desired space between tiles.

7. Continue setting the tiles, working your way up the wall. Use a level to ensure accurate alignment and squareness.

8. Remove the spacers and allow the Multi-Purpose Thin-Set to cure at least 48 hours before grouting.

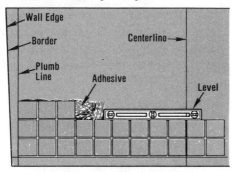

TILING COUNTERTOPS

Because a countertop is subject to a good deal of moisture, impact, and other abuse, it is important that high-quality tile is used. Install glazed tile around sinks and food preparation areas because unglazed tile tends to stain. Leave a 1/8" gap between plywood pieces for expansion.

If working over existing Formica, remove all residue from the surface. Rough up the surface with a coarse sanding disc to ensure a good bond. Be sure to remove all sanding dust.

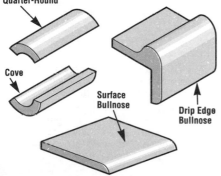

Various trim tile pieces are available for the tricky areas of a countertop, including the edges, corners, backsplash, and sink opening. They include surface bullnose, drip-edge bullnose, cove, and quarter-round pieces. For the neatest and most attractive look, a countertop should be covered only with whole tiles. However, since this is not always possible, you might want to install a self-rimming sink instead of mounting the sink below the tile; the rim does a nice job of covering the cut edges.

SETTING COUNTERTOP TILE

While tiling a countertop involves a good deal of careful planning, it is not as difficult as many people believe. Use the following procedure:

1. Starting with trim pieces or bullnose tiles and continuing with full tiles, make a dry run of the entire sink. If the counter is L-shaped, start the run at the inside corner and work outward both ways. Use a full tile for the corner piece; all trim pieces should be laid out with the grout lines following those of the rest of the tiles.

2. When the front and back edges are in position, make a dry run of the tiles around the sink. If the sink is self-rimming, lay the tiles in place and mark the cutlines from underneath. If the sink has a recessed basin, cut and trim the tile to fit around it.

3. Mark and cut tiles for faucet holes and any other openings as shown in the illustration.

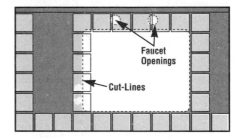

4. When you are satisfied with the entire layout, mark the tiles and/or the countertop with the necessary cut marks. Do all cutting before beginning tile installation.

5. The procedures for cutting, setting, and grouting countertop tile are identical to those outlined earlier. To prevent mildew, apply QUIKRETE® Tile and Grout Sealer about two weeks after the installation.

Building with Glass Block

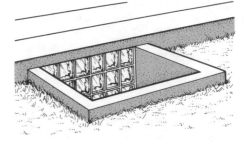

Besides admitting as much as 80% of outdoor light to dark areas, glass block also provides security, privacy, and noise reduction to your home. By using QUIKRETE® Glass Block Mortar, the installation is easy and long lasting. To lay 100 square feet of 6" block, you'll need 10 50-lb. bags; to lay 100 square feet of 8" block, 7 50-lb. bags are needed; and to lay 100 square feet of 12" block, 5 50-lb. bags of QUIKRETE® Glass Block Mortar must be used.

An important point to keep in mind is this: glass block can never be used as a load-bearing building material. Structural support is a must above, below, and on both sides of any glass block assembly. You'll also need to make allowances for expansion and anchoring, as described in the following procedures.

Tools and Materials

QUIKRETE® Glass Block Mortar
QUIKRETE® Acrylic Fortifier (optional)
Plastic connectors (optional)
Glass blocks, polyethylene foam or
   fiberglass expansion strips, anchors,
   reinforcing bars, and spacers
Trowel, rubber mallet, sponge or
   cloths, and level

STANDARD MORTAR METHOD

1. Secure expansion strips to the headers and jambs.

2. Lay a full bed of QUIKRETE® Glass Block Mortar on the sill. Set the first course of blocks, using spacers and a level to ensure straightness. Tap each block into position with a rubber mallet or a trowel fitted with a rubber-tipped handle. Once a block is in place, do not shift its position.

3. Fill all joints completely, maintaining a 1/4" to 3/8" mortar joint between blocks.

4. Lay a full mortar bed on top of the first course. Set the second course of blocks and fill the joints as before.

5. As you build the wall higher, the weight of the blocks may begin to force mortar out of the lower joints. If this happens, stop and let the mortar set before resuming the work.

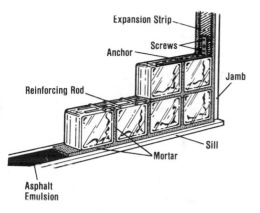

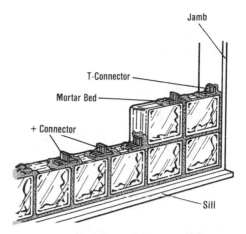

6. For stability, reinforcement must be added every 24" vertically. To do this, first lay a 1/8" bed of QUIKRETE® Glass Block Mortar on top of the installed block and press reinforcing bars lightly into the mortar.

7. Set an anchor every 24" vertically on top of the bars; at least 1' of each anchor should extend from the jamb. Lay another 1/8" mortar bed over top of the reinforcing bars and anchors.

8. Before the mortar hardens, tool all joints to make them smooth and concave.

9. Remove all excess mortar from the faces of the blocks with a damp sponge or cloth.

10. After allowing the mortar to cure for at least 1 full day, apply sealer between the blocks, headers, and jambs.

11. Give the faces of the blocks a final cleaning with clean water and a soft cloth. Do not use harsh cleaners, acids, or alkalines on glass block. Also, never use steel wool or a wire brush to clean glass block, because they will cause scratches.

USING MORTAR AND PLASTIC CONNECTORS

In this method, the previously described procedure for mortaring glass block is combined with plastic connectors to produce a structure of improved rigidity. The connectors also aid in alignment and spacing of the blocks, resulting in a more professional-looking job. Because all of the blocks rest on the connectors, there is no problem with the upper courses squeezing the mortar out of the lower courses. This enables you to work at your own pace, without constantly stopping to wait for the mortar to set. In addition, the connectors cannot be seen; they are buried in the mortar and therefore do not ruin the visual effect.

Plastic connectors are available to fit all sizes and thicknesses of glass block. There are two basic types of connector: a T-shaped design that can be used around the perimeter of the structure, and a plus-shaped design for use in internal joints. If you're planning a curved wall, tapered connectors are also available. Because T-shaped connectors are nailed or screwed in place, they serve as additional anchoring devices.

When placing T-shaped connectors prior to setting the first course of blocks, mortar them in place to prevent slippage. Once the first course has been laid, both types of connectors can be installed in the joints and mortared down as part of the mortar bed for the next course. Use a rubber mallet to tap each block down so that it fits tightly on the connectors below.

For Best Results

Refer to page 179 for more information on choosing and working with glass block.

While plastic connectors add structural rigidity to any glass block installation, they should be used in combination with, never in place of, reinforcing bars and anchors. These basic methods of reinforcement must always be used.

When installing anchors, bend them horizontally into the joint for added strength.

Mortarless Block Construction with QUIKWALL®

Surface Bonding Cement

QUIKWALL® Surface Bonding Cement (SBC) now makes most block construction possible without using mortar; it's literally a "stack and stucco" project. A single coat on dry-stacked block gives a handsome stucco finish and provides greater flexural and impact strength than mortar with less expense. A 50-pound bag will cover approximately 50 square feet at a 1/8″ thickness. In planning your project, note that actual rather than nominal block size is used since joints are not buttered.

BLOCK WALLS

The same basic techniques of wall construction are used no matter what your project happens to be.

Tools and Materials

QUIKWALL® Surface Bonding Cement
QUIKRETE® Concrete Acrylic Fortifier
QUIKRETE® Sand Mix or QUIK-RETE® All-Purpose Sand (if needed)
QUIKRETE® Concrete Repair Caulk
Mason's line, level, concrete or joint trowels, and chalk line
Mason's hammer, brick set, straight-edge, metal tie bars, and metal lathe strips

---

CONSTRUCTION

1. Construct the footer for the wall. (Refer to *Footers for Walls*, page 11.)

2. To ensure square, accurate corners and straight walls, dry-lay the corner leads and first course and chalk mark the block positions on the footer. Use a level and mason's line for accuracy.

3. Remove the blocks and lay 1/8″ to 3/8″ bed of prepared QUIKWALL® SBC on the footer. This bed of QUIKWALL® SBC helps in leveling the first course if there are slight irregularities in the slab or footer. Re-lay the bottom course, checking alignment and level every 3 to 4 blocks.

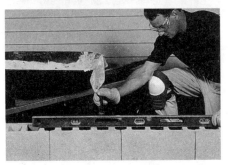

4. For projects with wall openings or intersecting walls (other than at corners), refer to steps 6 and 7. Otherwise, dry-stack the remaining block in a running bond pattern to the desired height, checking every few courses to maintain proper height. If necessary, shim with QUIKRETE® All-Purpose Sand or Sand Mix.

5. Wet down the wall and apply 1/8″ QUIKWALL® SBC coat to both the

sides and exposed ends of wall using a finishing trowel with an upward motion. If you must stop work, stop the QUIKWALL® SBC application on a block, not at a joint between blocks.

6. Stack and bond the main and bearing wall intersection together in 4- to 6-course intervals. After the main wall has been stacked and coated no higher than 6 courses, begin constructing the intersecting wall. It too should be placed and leveled in a 1/8″ to 3/8″ bed of QUIKWALL® SBC. Embed metal ties every 4 to 6 courses as shown. Stuffing the bottom of the block cell opening with paper will allow you to fill it with mortar to hold the tie. Continue to build the intersection in intervals to the full height of the wall.

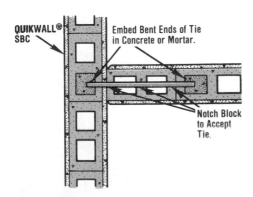

QUIKWALL® SBC

Embed Bent Ends of Tie in Concrete or Mortar.

Notch Block to Accept Tie.

7. To construct window or door openings, dry-stack the block no more than 2 or 3 courses higher than the bottom of the opening before framing out the opening to exact dimensions. The wall is then built up around the frame. Precast lintels make finishing the top of doors and windows easy. Because precast lintels are nonporous, the QUIKWALL® Surface Bonding Cement applied over the lintel must be fortified with QUIKRETE® Concrete Acrylic Fortifier. Simply lay the lintel in place and coat it with the fortified QUIKWALL® SBC mix.

8. Vertical control joints are needed to handle stresses and prevent cracking of the block or QUIKWALL® SBC finish. Spacing between control joints is determined by wall height. In general the ratio of control joint spacing to wall height is about 2:1. That is a 2′ high wall should have control joints every 4′, a 4′ wall every 8′, and an 8′ wall every 16′ to 20′. Control joints are also needed at the following points of weakness and/or high stress concentration.

- At all abrupt changes in wall height
- At all changes in wall thickness, such as those at pipe or duct chases and those adjacent to columns or pilasters
- Above joints in foundations and floors
- Below joints in roofs and floors that bear on the wall
- At a distance of not over half the allowable joint spacing from bonded intersections or corners
- At one or both sides of all door and window openings unless other crack control measures are used, i.e., joint reinforcement or bond beams

Regardless of the control joint design used, rake out the wall joint and caulk with QUIKRETE® Concrete Repair Caulk.

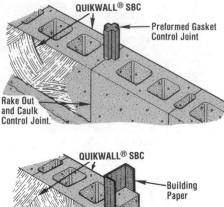

QUIKWALL® SBC

Preformed Gasket
Control Joint

Rake Out
and Caulk
Control Joint.

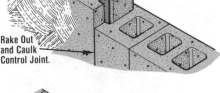

QUIKWALL® SBC

Building
Paper

Rake Out
and Caulk
Control Joint.

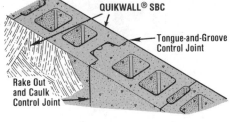

QUIKWALL® SBC

Tongue-and-Groove
Control Joint

Rake Out
and Caulk
Control Joint

For Best Results

Take extra care that the bottom course is laid properly, because each succeeding course will simply be stacked on it.

To ensure proper bonding, make certain that the blocks are clean and free of any dirt, soil, or grease.

Before laying the block, remove any burrs and chips from it with a hammer to get a tight fit.

Mix only as much QUIKWALL® SBC as can be used in 1 hour.

To obtain the finish you desire, experiment with different trowels and techniques before applying the QUIKWALL® SBC coat to your wall.

9. Attach capping sills to the top course by anchoring bolts firmly into the concrete or QUIKWALL® SBC . Moist-cure the wall after 8 hours by dampening with a fine spray. Repeat several times daily for 3 days. Roof or floor construction can proceed when the curing is complete.

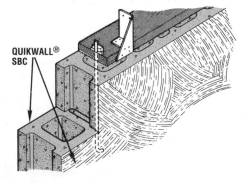

QUIKWALL®
SBC

Gallery of Mortarless Block Projects

Take a look at some of the things you can build using the technique of mortarless block construction.

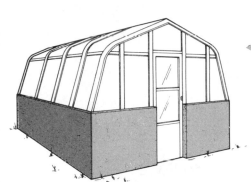

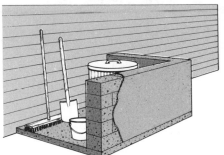

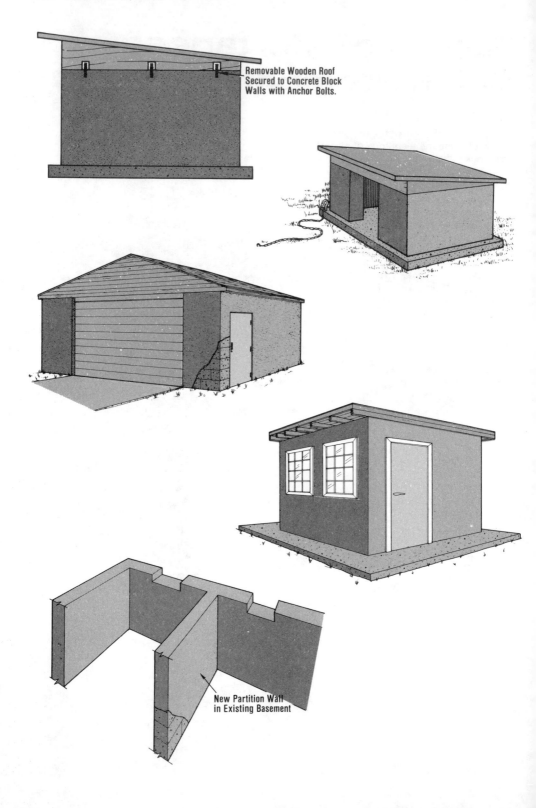

Removable Wooden Roof Secured to Concrete Block Walls with Anchor Bolts.

New Partition Wall in Existing Basement

Mobile Home Under- pinning

Mortarless block construction with QUIKWALL® Surface Bonding Cement is an ideal method of finishing off mobile home installations. When building up underpinning, plan the work so that the top course of block rests flush with the bottom of the mobile home.

Tools and Materials

See those listed under *Footers for Walls* (page 11) and *Mortarless Block Construction with QUIKWALL®* (page 104).

In addition, you will need sufficient amounts of vent block, drip cap, and quality caulking.

CONSTRUCTION

1. Use a plumb bob to locate the exact front of the wall and then construct a suitable footer (see page 11). Build up the wall as you would any other type of QUIKWALL® SBC installation (see page 104).

2. Mobile home underpinnings require ventilation. Special foundation vents equal in size to concrete block are available from building suppliers. These vents are simply included in the stacking pattern during construction. They should be placed in one of the middle courses every 10 to 12 blocks depending on local building codes.

3. Slope the final grade away from the home to prevent water from collecting against the block.

4. Caulk the joint between the home and top course of block and install a drip cap to prevent water penetration.

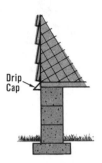

Drip Cap

Stuccoing

Stucco is an attractive and durable cement-based coating frequently applied to masonry and properly prepared wooden, gypsum wallboard, and expanded polystyrene insulation board surfaces. Stucco is usually white, but special color blends are available. Do your stuccoing in mild weather (50° to 80° F) and work when the surface is shielded from direct sun that could dry the stucco too quickly, resulting in cracking.

STUCCOING SYSTEMS

Stucco can be applied as a three-coat, two-coat, or one-coat system, depending on the type of stuccoing material used and the type of surface to which it is applied. QUIKRETE® manufactures stucco base coat and finish coat mixes for three- and two-coat applications, as well as a fiberglass-reinforced stucco mix intended for one-coat use.

THREE-COAT STUCCOING

Three-coat stucco is the oldest and most commonly used system. It is normally used when installing stucco over wooden sheathing, but can also be used on masonry surfaces if there is doubt as to their ability to hold the stucco securely.

A three-coat system uses a base of waterproof roofing paper that is covered with metal lath or 1" by 20 gauge wire mesh. The metal lath or wire mesh does not rest directly on the waterproof paper. It is attached with special self-furring

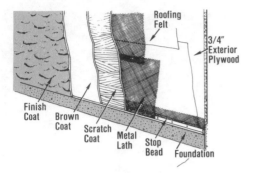

Finish Coat, Brown Coat, Scratch Coat, Metal Lath, Stop Bead, Foundation, Roofing Felt, 3/4" Exterior Plywood

nails that create a 1/4" space between the lath and paper. This space is needed for good stucco adhesion.

Self-furring nails are designed with a 1/4" plug surrounding the nail shaft. The plug is positioned behind the lath and against the wall. The lath is booked over the nail head and the nail is driven into the wall. Self-furring lath is also available. This product combines the lath and waterproof backing into a single roll. It is installed using ordinary roofing nails.

Metal stop beads are installed along the base and top of the wall and around window and door openings. These beads support the lath and stucco and allow moisture to escape from behind the stucco. Special corner beads are installed at outside corners to create true, even corners at these locations.

Tools and Materials

QUIKRETE® Base-Coat Stucco
QUIKRETE® Finish-Coat Stucco
Mixing box, mason's hoe, hawk, trowel, float, plaster rake, masonry brush, and screed board
Hammer, self-furring nails, 15-lb roofing felt or other waterproof backing paper, metal lath or wire mesh, and metal stop beads
Caulking gun and caulk

PREPARING THE SURFACE

1. Fasten the roofing felt or waterproof backing to the sheathing or other surface with galvanized nails. Each horizontal strip of backing should overlap the one below it by 3".

2. Install the metal stop beads at the bottom and top of the walls and around all doors and windows. Cut the beads to size using a metal snip or hacksaw. Nail the beads to the concrete founda-

tion or the edge of the wood sheathing. Be sure the beads are installed level and that sections are properly aligned.

3. Attach the lath, working from the bottom up. Rest the first sheet of lath or mesh in the stop bead that runs along the base of the wall. Fasten the lath or mesh with self-furring nails as just described.

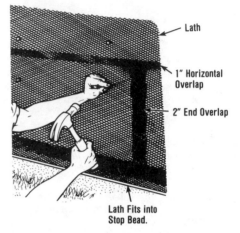

Lath, 1" Horizontal Overlap, 2" End Overlap, Lath Fits into Stop Bead.

4. Continue to install lath sheets. Successive sheets should overlap the one below it by 1", with end overlaps being 2" as shown. The metal lath should extend 3/4" beyond the corner beads at any outside corners.

CONTROL JOINTS

Undesirable cracking can be minimized by careful preparation and application of the stucco coats. But even with the finest job, cracks can develop due to many factors, including:

- Shrinkage stress
- Building movements
- Settling foundations
- Construction joints
- Intersecting walls or ceilings, corners, and pilasters
- Restraints from lighting and plumbing fixtures
- Weak sections due to cross-section changes, such as openings

While it is difficult to prevent all cracks, they can be largely controlled with the help of metal control joints. These stucco control joints should be installed directly over existing control joints in the underlying structure.

Walls and ceilings that use metal lath to anchor the stucco should be divided

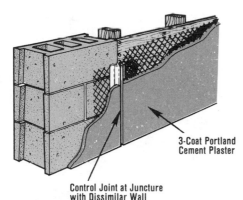

3-Coat Portland
Cement Plaster

Control Joint at Juncture
with Dissimilar Wall

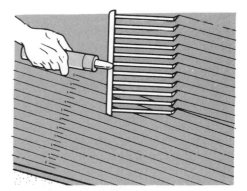

into rectangular panels with a control joint. Panels should be no larger than 144 square feet. The metal lath should not extend across these control joints. Use metal that is weather tight and corrosion resistant for control joints on exterior surfaces.

APPLYING THE SCRATCH COAT

1. Both the scratch or first coat and the brown or second coat are made using QUIKRETE® Base-Coat Stucco Mix. Add enough water to the mix to achieve a putty-like consistency, and prepare only enough mix that can be applied in about 1 hour.

2. Trowel the scratch coat onto the lath or mesh working from bottom to top. The scratch coat should be 3/8" thick. Force it through the wire mesh so that it fills the 1/4" gap between the mesh and wall completely.

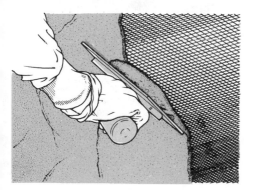

3. Smooth the scratch coat with the trowel.

4. After the scratch coat has set enough to be firm but not hard, use the rake to scratch horizontal grooves about 1/8"

deep across the face of the base coat mortar.

5. Mist the scratch coat periodically to ensure strong curing. When applying stucco over open-frame wood construction, wait at least 48 hours before applying the brown coat.

APPLYING THE BROWN COAT

The brown coat is the second coat of stucco. It too consists of QUIKRETE® Base-Coat Stucco Mix. The brown coat is applied to a thickness of 3/8". Take extreme care to apply the brown coat smooth and evenly. The finish coat is only 1/8" thick and will not hide bumps or irregularities in the brown coat surface.

1. Prepare only as much QUIKRETE® Base-Coat Stucco that can be applied in 1 hour.

2. Dampen the surface of the scratch coat with a fine spray of water, but do not soak it.

3. Use a trowel to apply the brown coat to a 3/8" thickness. Do the entire wall

section in one work session, otherwise a color difference might be seen through the finish coat.

4. Screed the brown coat evenly by running the edge of a straight board over the brown coat and smoothing out the high and low spots.

5. After the brown coat loses its sheen, float it smooth.

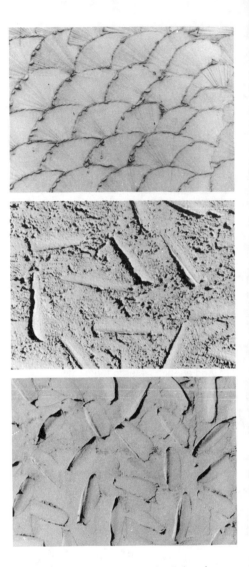

6. Moist-cure the brown coat for 2 days, and then air cure for 5 additional days before applying the finish coat.

APPLYING THE FINISH COAT

The finish coat is the third or top layer. It consists of QUIKRETE® Finish-Coat Stucco applied to a 1/8″ thickness.

1. Trowel the 1/8″ thick finish coat over the brown coat, starting at the bottom and working to the top of the wall. As with the brown coat, mix only enough stucco that can be applied in 1 hour and complete the entire wall or major section in one session to reduce possible color variations.

2. QUIKRETE® Finish-Coat Stucco readily accepts any number of popular textured finishes. Depending on the desired texture and finish, the coat can be applied evenly or unevenly. You can give an even texture distinctive finishes by lining it using a broom, slapping it with a leafy branch or the mason's brush, or by flinging small gobs onto it and floating them almost flush with the smooth layer. Several finishes are shown here.

3. Moist-cure the finish coat for 5 days by misting it periodically with a fine spray.

4. Seal all the joints around doors and windows with a masonry-compatible caulk.

5. QUIKRETE® Finish-Coat Stucco can be colored prior to application, eliminating the need for painting. Simply add liquid QUIKRETE® Stucco and Mortar Color directly to the mixing water before it is added to the dry QUIKRETE® Finish-Coat Stucco Mix.

TWO-COAT STUCCOING

Two-coat stuccoing is often used when stucco is applied directly to concrete or masonry surfaces without the use of lath or wire mesh. This is because the masonry or concrete provides a very rigid and stable base. In a two-coat application, the brown coat is eliminated and the finish coat is applied directly to the scratch coat. As shown in the illustration, the scratch coat of QUIKRETE® Base-Coat Stucco is applied to a 3/8″ thickness, grooved, and cured as in a three-coat system. The top coat of QUIKRETE® Finish-Coat Stucco is then applied to a 1/4″ thickness and textured as desired.

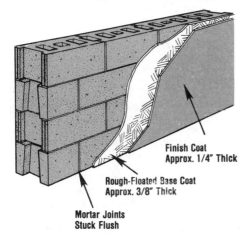

Finish Coat
Approx. 1/4″ Thick

Rough-Floated Base Coat
Approx. 3/8″ Thick

Mortar Joints
Stuck Flush

Tools and Materials

QUIKRETE® Base-Coat Stucco
QUIKRETE® Finish-Coat Stucco
Mixing box, mason's hoe, hawk, trowel, float, plaster rake, masonry brush, and screed board
QUIKRETE® Concrete Acrylic Fortifier
Caulking gun and caulk

SURFACE PREPARATION

Concrete or masonry surfaces must be sufficiently rough and porous to provide proper adhesion for the base coat in a two-coat system. You can test the surface porosity by spraying it with clean water. Note how quickly the moisture is absorbed. Porous, strong bonding surfaces such as concrete or cinder-based block will usually absorb water readily.

Troweled concrete walls may be too dense to absorb sufficient water. This is the case if water droplets form from the spray and run down the wall surface.

The addition of 1/2 gallon of QUIKRETE® Concrete Acrylic Fortifier as part of the mix water for each 80-pound bag of QUIKRETE® Finish-Coat Stucco Mix used to form the scratch coat layer will provide sufficient holding power on slightly rough surfaces.

Concrete and masonry surfaces should be free of oil, dirt, or other materials that could weaken the bond. Paint must be removed from painted concrete or masonry to improve the bonding characteristics of the scratch coat.

APPLICATION

1. Locate and construct control joints as in three-coat stucco systems described earlier in this section.

2. Application of the 3/8″ thick scratch coat and 1/4″ finish coat is similar to three-coat procedures described earlier. Make certain to cure the scratch coat for at least 24 hours before applying the finish coat.

ONE-COAT STUCCOING

QUIKWALL® Fiber-Reinforced Stucco (FRS) is an alkali-resistant glass fiber-reinforced stucco intended to be used as a one-coat stucco over exterior rigid insulation board or non-insulated exterior-approved sheathing, such as Type-X gypsum board. The one-coat QUIKWALL® FRS is applied to a minimum thickness of 3/8″ and can be textured as desired. It provides a high-impact, crack-resistant shell.

SHEATHING AND RIGID INSULATION

In non-insulated installations, the thickness and type of sheathing must match all local and national building codes governing your area, so check with local building authorities during the planning stages of the project.

In insulated installations, the expanded polystyrene board must meet the AFM manufacturing specifications for AFMWSGEPS,ICBO Evaluation Report No. 4169. Your building supplier should be able to confirm this for you when you purchase the insulation.

Insulation panels should be tongue-and-groove design with a minimum tongue height of 3/8″, unless local codes specify differently. Install the panels in a horizontal position with the tongues facing upward. All panel edges must butt on an underlying stud, and vertical butt joints should be staggered when they occur other than at corners or against metal trim. The insulation board can be installed over a waterproof membrane according to local codes.

SURFACE PREPARATION

Surface preparation for one-coat QUIKWALL® FRS stuccoing over approved sheathing or insulation panels is similar to that used in standard three-coat stuccoing covered earlier.

THE QUIKWALL® FRS is applied to a minimum thickness of 3/8″ over a base consisting of a waterproof backing paper covered by 1″ by 20-gauge galvanized wire mesh. The mesh may be either self-furred or furred using self-furring nails as in the three-coat system discussed earlier. As with three-coat systems, the 1/4″ space between the backing paper and the mesh is critical for the project's success. Metal capping is also installed at the top and bottom of the wall and along windows and doors. Control joints must also be installed as in three-coat systems.

Tools and Materials

QUIKWALL® Fiberglass-Reinforced Stucco
QUIKRETE® Concrete Acrylic Fortifier
Mixing box, mason's hoe, hawk, trowel, and masonary brush
Hammer, self-furring nails, 15-lb. roofing felt or other waterproof backing paper, metal lath or wire mesh, and metal stop beads
Caulking gun and caulk

APPLICATION

1. QUIKRETE® Concrete Acrylic Fortifier can be added as part of the mix water to provide greater impact-resistance, strength, and durability. Use 1/2 gallon of QUIKRETE® Concrete Acrylic Fortifier for each 80-pound bag of FRS.

2. Mix to a smooth, butter-like consistency.

3. Apply the QUIKWALL® Fiberglass-Reinforced Stucco using a trowel. Work from the top to the bottom. Force the mix through the mesh so that it fills the 1/4″ gap between the mesh and waterproof paper completely.

4. Work to maintain an even 3/8″ or slightly thicker coating. Texture the finish as the QUIKWALL® FRS is applied.

5. QUIKWALL® Liquid Stucco may be trowel applied over QUIKWALL® FRS to provide a moisture resistant color and texture coating. QUIKWALL® Liquid Stucco is available in three textures – Swirl, Coarse Sanded and Fine Sanded. It can be pigmented to any desired color.

For Best Results

Apply the brown coat and finish coat to an entire wall at a time to avoid coloration differences.

While applying stucco, do not try to get tight joints around windows and doors. The caulk will take care of sealing the joints.

Do not rake the scratch coat so hard that stucco is removed. Only rake hard enough to score the coat. A piece of lath or a wooden block with nails driven into it will also do a good job of raking.

Do not apply stucco to a frozen surface or when freezing temperatures are likely.

Insulating Foundation Walls

If your house has uninsulated concrete basement walls, you can reduce heat loss substantially by installing rigid insulation covered with QUIKWALL® Fiberglass-Reinforced Foundation Coating or Foam Coating. Panels can be made of extruded polystyrene foam (blue board), expanded polystyrene (white bead board), urethane

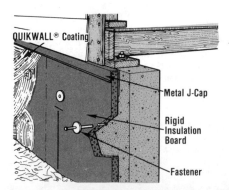

QUIKWALL® Coating

Metal J-Cap

Rigid Insulation Board

Fastener

panels, pressed glass fiberboard, or other rigid insulation materials that have sufficient strength. For certain extruded insulation boards with a film coating present on the board face, it is necessary to remove this coating by stripping off the film. For other extruded boards having a slick surface, you must roughen the surface to insure proper bond. This is accomplished by sanding or scarifying the surface. Insulation panels may be applied to any structurally sound foundation wall.

Ideally, the insulation panels should extend below the frost line. If digging to the frost line level is not practical, the panels should extend a minimum of 6" below ground level.

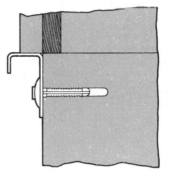

5. Mechanically fasten the channel to the foundation by installing fasteners through the drilled holes.

INSTALLING THE INSULATION

The rigid board can be secured to the foundation with special concrete fasteners and washers or with panel and foam adhesives specially formulated for use with rigid insulation board.

1. Measure and cut the insulation panel to size using a saw or utility knife. (With certain types of extruded polystyrene boards, the clear plastic coating must be removed prior to installation.) Make certain all panels butt tightly against one another and the J-channel.

2. If securing with fasteners and washers, it is recommended that a small amount of the proper adhesive be used to help hold the panel in place while the mechanical fasteners are being installed. Predrill the proper size holes through the rigid board into the foundation on 24" centers both vertically and horizontally. Holes must be deep enough to accommodate the fasteners and allow the washers to be recessed into the panel. Butt the panels at the corners so one panel overlaps the other.

Tools and Materials

QUIKWALL® Fiberglass-Reinforced Foundation Coating or Foam Coating Rigid insulation panels, fiberglass tape, fasteners and washers, medium-heavy paintbrush, acrylic latex or silicone caulk, caulking gun, metal J-channel capping, hammer, shovel, straightedge, tape measure, saw or utility knife, putty knife, and trowel Power drill with mixing paddle

---

WALL PREPARATION

To estimate the amount of rigid board needed, measure from the bottom edge of the siding to the below-grade depth and multiply by the perimeter of the house. This will give you the square footage of board needed. To prepare for installation do the following:

1. Dig out the soil from the foundation to the required depth.

2. J-channel or other metal capping must be installed at the bottom edge of the siding and around all windows and doors to protect the exposed edge of the rigid insulation. To install, first apply a bead of caulking to the underside of the bottom edge of the siding.

3. Drill properly sized holes in the channel on 2' centers. The exact size of the hole will depend on the fasteners used to mount the channel.

4. Press the channel into the caulking bead to create a watertight seal behind the J-channel. This prevents water from flowing down behind the insulation.

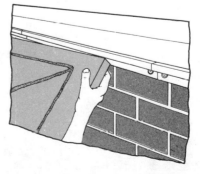

3. If securing with an adhesive, use only those adhesives designed to be used with rigid foam insulation. Solvent-based construction adhesives will destroy the installation board. Apply the adhesive according to the manufacturer's instructions.

4. Apply self-sticking fiberglass tape to the joints between the insulation panels, to all outside corners, using two or more overlapping pieces as needed, and over all fastener heads and damaged panel areas. Brush dirt and residue from the insulation surface. Note: Foam insulation that has been exposed to sunlight may have a powdery, yellow residue on its surface that must be removed.

5. Mask around channels, windows, and doors to prevent contact with the masonry coating.

APPLYING THE COATING

1. Remove the bag of powdered contents from the bucket and place 1 gallon of water into the bucket.

2. Using the mixing paddle installed on the power drill, begin mixing the water while adding the powdered material. It may be necessary to add a little more water to obtain the desired final consistency once all the powder has been added.

3. Once all the powder is added, continue mixing for no more than 5 minutes. If the mix begins to stiffen during application, remix, adding a *slight* amount of water, if needed.

4. Use a putty knife to precoat all taped areas with QUIKWALL® mix.

5. With a brush or trowel, cover the insulation panels to the desired thickness. To prevent extreme color variation, cover the entire wall corner-to-corner in one work session. (Note: A uniform color is not possible with gray portland cement.) Clean the brush or trowel periodically to avoid a buildup

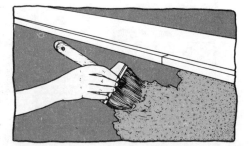

of coating. Texture the coating as desired while it is applied. Do not rewet the coating for the purpose of texturing.

6. The final coating thickness should be approximately 1/16", although a thicker coating can be applied if the surface must withstand abuse. The final coat is best applied with a stiff-bristled brush.

FINISHING AND CURING

1. Remove all masking tape.

2. Replace the dirt from around the foundation, sloping it so that water runs away from the foundation.

3. Caulk around channels, doors, and windows to prevent moisture from penetrating behind the coating.

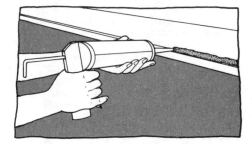

4. Moist-cure the surface of the coating using a fine mist spray after the surface has set (about 2 hours). Continue the misting several times daily for a minimum of 2 days.

5. If desired, the coated panels can be brush coated with QUIKRETE® Masonry Coating in a variety of colors. They can also be painted for a dense color finish. (See page 36 for further details.)

Well Collars

When installing a well, the casing must extend above the ground at least 6" (preferably a full foot) in order to keep out groundwater. A concrete well collar placed around the protruding end of the casing provides drainage as well as an effective, watertight seal. Simply place

QUIKRETE® Fast-Setting Concrete Mix in a 2′ radius around the casing. Pack the dry mix around the casing and add water. The method is similar to setting posts, covered on page 39. Use a trowel to slope it away from the casing as shown in the illustration.

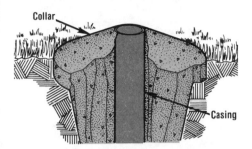

Collar

Casing

SECTION II: REPAIR AND MAINTENANCE WITH QUIKRETE®

While it is true that masonry is one of the most long-lasting and durable types of construction, some form of maintenance and/or repair work will eventually be needed. In this section, you'll learn how to deal with routine repairs, such as surface cracks and flaking concrete, as well as more involved procedures like tuck-pointing mortar joints and repairing sunken brick. We've also included helpful tips designed to save you time and money. And remember, QUIKRETE® has a full line of masonry repair products on hand to help you get the job done as quickly and as easily as possible.

Repairing Concrete

Cracks, chips, and broken or flaking areas in concrete are not only unsightly, they can lead to further deterioration of the surface. The result is a costly replacement project as opposed to a simple repair. Inspect your concrete and masonry walls, walks, and slabs for damage on a regular basis. Early spring is an excellent time to assess any damage from winter freeze/thaw cycles.

When repairing concrete it's important to select the right repair product for the job. A product ideally suited for general patching may not work well on small cracks and fractures. And not all products are suited for overlaying large areas. That's why QUIKRETE® offers a complete line of concrete repair products formulated to meet all your patching and repair needs.

MINOR CRACKS AND FRACTURES

Small cracks and fractures 1/8″ to 1/2″ wide are often difficult to patch using cement-based products. There's just no way to force the mixture into such a small opening. QUIKRETE® Gray Concrete Crack Seal and QUIKRETE® Concrete Repair Caulk solve this problem. Gray Concrete Crack Seal is a thick liquid that can be poured directly into cracks in walks, slabs, and other horizontal surfaces. Concrete Repair Caulk is a textured sealant that can be applied to cracks in walls and other vertical surfaces.

Tools and Materials

QUIKRETE® Gray Concrete Crack Seal
QUIKRETE® Concrete Repair Caulk
QUIKRETE® Concrete & Asphalt Cleaner
QUIKRETE® All-Purpose Sand
Scrub brush, wire brush, and caulking gun

MINOR CRACKS IN HORIZONTAL SURFACES

1. Use a wire brush or similar tool to clean all dirt, concrete chips, and

organic matter from the crack. Clean grease and heavy dirt deposits using QUIKRETE® Concrete & Asphalt Cleaner.

2. Shake bottle of QUIKRETE® Gray Concrete Crack Seal. Cut the tip of the bottle so the opening matches the width of the cracks to be repaired. If the crack is deep, fill to within 1/4″ of the surface with QUIKRETE® All-Purpose Sand.

3. Apply the sealer in 1/4″ layers. Allow each 1/4″ layer to setup overnight before applying the next layer.

MINOR CRACKS IN VERTICAL SURFACES

1. Clean the crack as just described.
2. Cut tip of QUIKRETE® Concrete Repair Caulk tube on an angle to make a 1/4″ to 3/8″ hole. Use cartridge in standard caulking gun.
3. Apply by pushing cartridge tip over surface and forcing bead of Concrete Repair deep into the crack. Apply no thicker than 3/8″ at a time.

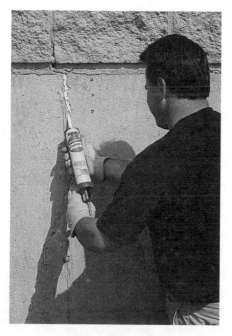

For Best Results

On hot days, cool the caulking tube in your refrigerator for an hour or so before application. The caulk will run less and be easier to apply.

Use QUIKRETE® Concrete Repair Caulk to seal joints where concrete and masonry meet wooden or metal framing or other surfaces. Fill the joint completely and slightly overlap the caulk onto the adjacent surfaces.

LARGER CRACKS AND HOLES IN VERTICAL SURFACES

Wide, deep cracks and holes in concrete blocks and concrete walls require patching with a cement based repair product. QUIKRETE® Quick-Setting Cement is an excellent product for this type of repair because it has superior bonding capabilities.

Tools and Materials

QUIKRETE® Quick-Setting Cement
QUIKRETE® Concrete Acrylic Fortifier
QUIKRETE® Concrete & Asphalt Cleaner
Cold chisel, hammer, wire brush, broom, safety glasses or goggles, sponge, pointing trowel, and finishing trowel

1. Clean the loose concrete and dirt from the damaged area using the hammer, chisel, and a wire brush. Clean grease and dirt from the area to be repaired with QUIKRETE® Concrete & Asphalt Cleaner. Rinse the area thoroughly.

2. Make sure to dampen the area to be repaired before mixing the patching material.

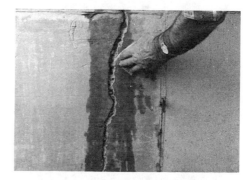

3. Mix the QUIKRETE® Quick-Setting Cement with water according to the directions on the package. If the area

to be repaired is less than 1″ deep x 1″ wide, add QUIKRETE® Concrete Acrylic Fortifier to the mix water. Keep in mind the QUIKRETE® Quick-Setting Cement is a stiff mix and will have the consistency of modeling clay.

4. Press the patching material as deep as possible into the area to be repaired using a pointing trowel or similar tool. Completely fill the area to be repaired.

5. Use a steel finishing trowel to compact the repair and screed off any excess material. Feather edge the patching material onto the adjoining surfaces to create a smooth, clean repair.

6. Mist the repair area several times daily to promote better curing and a strong bond. (This step is not necessary if QUIKRETE® Concrete Acrylic Fortifier was mixed with the QUIKRETE® Quick-Setting Cement.)

For Best Results

Keep the trowel clean and damp when applying QUIKRETE® Quick-Setting Cement. This will keep the mix from curling up on the trowel.

Do not add too much water to the QUIKRETE® Quick-Setting Cement during mixing. Mix only as much material as can be placed in 10 minutes.

LARGER CRACKS AND HOLES IN HORIZONTAL SURFACES

For wider cracks or damaged areas of concrete up to one square foot in size, use QUIKRETE® Vinyl Concrete Patcher. Vinyl Concrete Patcher is an excellent product for repairing isolated patches of crumbling or pitted concrete up to a depth of 1/2″. Because it contains fine sand and vinyl resins, it can be troweled to a finish as thin as 1/16″ so it is smooth with the surrounding concrete.

1. Vigorously rub the wire brush over the flaking concrete to loosen all damaged concrete. The tip of the trowel can be used to pry up loose sections of the flaked concrete.

2. Sweep away all loose particles and dust.

3. If needed, clean the surface using QUIKRETE® Concrete & Asphalt Cleaner. Rinse with clean water. Do not leave any standing water on the surface to be repaired.

4. Apply the QUIKRETE® Vinyl Concrete Patcher with a trowel. Feather edge the patching mixture out onto the surrounding concrete to create a smooth repair.

5. Apply the patcher in 1/4″ layers. If the hole is deeper than 1/4″, apply the patcher in stages, allowing each layer to cure for several days before applying the next layer.

For patches greater in depth than 1/2″, but less than 2″, QUIKRETE® Sand Mix should be used.

1. Undercut the edges of the repair area at least 1″ below the surface using a hammer and cold chisel. Brush out all loose concrete, dust, and other material until there is a solid base for the repair.

2. Clean the exposed area as needed, using QUIKRETE® Concrete & Asphalt Cleaner to remove grease, oil, or stubborn dirt.

3. If the repair is 1" to 2", apply a coat of QUIKRETE® Concrete Bonding Adhesive to the surface after it has dried. Brush the adhesive on as thick as a coat of paint.

4. Allow the Bonding Adhesive to dry completely before applying the patching material.

5. Mix the QUIKRETE® Sand Mix with water to a plastic-like consistency.

6. Press the sand mix into the hole. Immediately smooth and level the patch using a trowel.

7. After the sand mix patch has lost its water sheen, trowel the area to desired finish.

OVERLAYING LARGER SURFACES

QUIKRETE® Latex Cement is a two-part repair product consisting of a special latex powder and liquid latex bonding agent. This material is made for patching and smoothing concrete and masonry surfaces over larger areas. It can be applied from a thickness of 1/16" to a full 1/4". QUIKRETE® Latex Cement can be used indoors and out, and as an underlayment or finished wear surface. It is designed for long-lasting, durable repairs.

Tools and Materials

QUIKRETE® Latex Cement
QUIKRETE® Concrete & Asphalt
  Cleaner
Scrub brush, broom, wire brush, trowel, large mixing container, and straightedge

---

SURFACE PREPARATION

1. Remove all loose flakes, dirt, and dust from repair area.

2. Scrub away grease, oil, and stubborn dirt using QUIKRETE® Concrete & Asphalt Cleaner.

3. Dampen the surface to be repaired with clean water, but do not leave standing water.

MIXING AND APPLICATION

Each pail of QUIKRETE® Latex Cement contains a 44-pound bag of latex cement powder and a 1-gallon jug of latex bonding agent.

1. Pour most of the latex bonding agent into a clean container and gradually mix in all of the latex cement powder.

2. Slowly add in additional amounts of latex bonding agent until the desired workable consistency is achieved. Do not add water to the mix.

3. Do not mix more cement than can be placed in 20 minutes. Avoid overmixing in mechanical mixers. It can lead to air entrapment and a reduced bond.

4. Apply the latex cement to the surface using a large finishing trowel. Apply pressure to ensure a good bond.

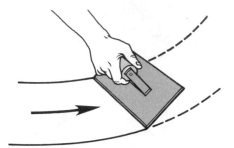

5. Run a straightedge back and forth over the repaired area to level the patching material.

6. If desired, trowel the surface to a smoother finish.

7. Under normal circumstances, QUIKRETE® Latex Cement does not require moist-curing. But in hot, windy, or low humidity conditions, it is best to moist-cure the overlayment for at least 48 hours.

For Best Results

Do not use QUIKRETE® Latex Cement when the temperature is expected to fall below 40° F within the next 48 hours.

For fills deeper than 1/4" apply QUIKRETE® Latex Cement in layers, allowing for curing between applications. Deeper fills up to 2" deep should be filled with QUIKRETE® Sand Mix and QUIKRETE® Concrete Bonding Adhesive as described earlier in this section.

Repairing Steps

Tools and Materials

QUIKRETE® Quick-Setting Cement
or QUIKRETE® Sand Mix
QUIKRETE® Concrete Bonding
Adhesive
QUIKRETE® Concrete Acrylic
Fortifier
QUIKRETE® Concrete & Asphalt
Cleaner
Cold chisel, ball peen hammer, goggles and gloves, pointing trowel,
plasterer's trowel, and paintbrush
Scrap lumber (for wood forms)

2. For repairs less than 1″ deep, mix QUIKRETE® Concrete Acrylic Fortifier with the Quick-Setting Cement or Sand Mix.

3. Mix 5-1/2 parts Quick-Setting Cement to 1 part liquid. Mix only long enough to obtain a smooth consistency and mix no more than can be applied in 10 minutes.

4. Dampen the surface and apply the mix.

5. Allow the Quick-Setting Cement to gain its initial set (5 to 10 minutes) and then sculpt the patch by scraping and shaving with the trowel edge.

For Best Results

In hot, dry conditions, keep the patch moist for 24 hours. Cover with plastic film.

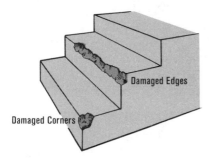

Damage on concrete steps usually occurs at the leading edges of the tread or at corners.

1. Undercut and widen the broken area with a cold chisel and hammer. Remove all dirt and loose concrete and clean with Concrete & Asphalt Cleaner.

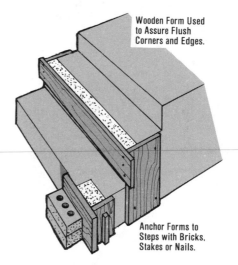

Wooden Form Used to Assure Flush Corners and Edges.

Anchor Forms to Steps with Bricks, Stakes or Nails.

Include Wood Molding in the Forms for more Decorative, Protruding Stair Treads.

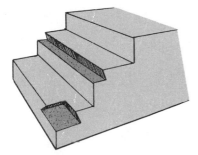

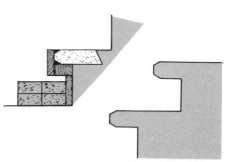

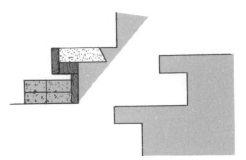

Do not sculpt until the Quick-Setting Cement is hard enough to retain a thumbprint.

Use forms for larger repairs or when the tread projects out from the riser.

For repairs deeper than 2″, see following section on *Repairing Badly Pitted/Chipped Concrete Surfaces.*

Repairing Badly Pitted/ Chipped Concrete Surfaces

Tools and Materials

QUIKRETE® Sand Mix
QUIKRETE® Concrete & Asphalt
  Cleaner
QUIKRETE® Concrete Bonding
  Adhesive
QUIKRETE® Concrete Acrylic Fortifier
QUIKRETE® Concrete Mix (for pour-
  ing depths over 2″)
Pickax, shovel, hammer or half-
  hatchet, saw, level, finishing trowel,
  bricklayer's trowel, edger, broom,
  cold chisel, ball-peen hammer,
  sledgehammer, and safety goggles
Forming lumber and stakes
Wheelbarrow
Curing materials

Use QUIKRETE® Sand Mix to resurface damaged concrete to depths up to 2″. For patches less than 1″ thick, replace part of the mixing water with QUIKRETE® Concrete Acrylic Fortifier. If the topping is from 1″ to 2″ thick, first coat the damaged area with QUIKRETE® Concrete Bonding Adhesive, and mix the Sand Mix with water only.

For depths greater than 2″, use QUIKRETE® Concrete Mix to build up the damaged area and then cap with a 2″ topping coat of Sand Mix.

SITE PREPARATION

1. Dig a small trench along the edge of the damaged surface so that forms can be set in place level with the old concrete surface.

2. Remove all broken and loose concrete, dirt, dust, and plant remains to form a sound base for the new topping. Use QUIKRETE® Concrete & Asphalt Cleaner to remove dirt or grease stains.

3. Set and stake forms against the old sidewalk or slab. Backfill against the forms to ensure sufficient support.

4. Use a level to make sure that the forms are set at the correct height and that there is adequate slope for drainage.

MAKING THE REPAIR

1. If damage in some areas is deeper than 2", use QUIKRETE® Concrete Mix to fill these low spots to within 1" or so of final grade. This reduces the amount of QUIKRETE® Sand Mix required for the job. Begin by coating

these low spots with QUIKRETE® Concrete Bonding Adhesive.

2. Wait until the bonding adhesive dries.

3. Mix a sufficient amount of QUIKRETE® Concrete Mix and fill in the low spots, especially along form edges.

4. The final 1" topping is made of QUIKRETE® Sand Mix. When this layer is less than 1", add QUIKRETE® Concrete Acrylic Fortifier as part of the Sand Mix liquid. **Note:** For Sand

Mix toppings thicker than 1", but less than 2", do not use Acrylic Fortifier. Instead, apply QUIKRETE® Concrete Bonding Adhesive to the surface as in Steps 1 and 2. Sand Mix containing Acrylic Fortifier should never come in direct contact with Concrete Bonding Adhesive. In this job, the concrete mix patch separates the adhesive and fortified sand mix.

5. Mix the QUIKRETE® Sand Mix until a plastic-like consistency is obtained.

6. Trowel the Sand Mix onto the damaged area. Use heavy trowel pressure to work the material onto the surface; then build up material to the proper depth.

7. Trowel the surface smooth using a steel finishing trowel. Edge using a concrete edger if desired.

8. To assure a nonskid surface apply a broom finish. Always pull the broom toward you, use light pressure, and do not overlap the strokes.

9. Cure the new surface with QUIKRETE® Acrylic Concrete Cure & Seal. Apply after finishing when surface sheen has disappeared and new surface has hardened.

For Best Results

Avoid using patching material during extremely hot or cold weather.

Break up badly broken concrete with a sledgehammer and make a new pour. Use some of the broken pieces of the old concrete to take up space in the new pour. Install steel reinforcement rods where extra support is needed.

Follow the general finishing tips given in the projects section *Concrete Sidewalks and Small Slabs.*

Repairing Concrete Walks

Over a number of years, even correctly placed concrete sidewalks can be badly damaged and cracked by impacts, severe freeze/thaw cycles, and grade changes caused by such things as tree growth. Minor problems can be corrected by using the methods discussed in *Repairing Concrete* (page 120). For more serious damage, follow the steps below, which are similar to those previously described.

Tools and Materials

QUIKRETE® Fiber-Reinforced Concrete Mix or QUIKRETE® Concrete Mix
QUIKRETE® Concrete Bonding Adhesive
QUIKRETE® Concrete & Asphalt Cleaner
QUIKRETE® Acrylic Concrete Cure & Seal
Sledgehammer or pick, chisel, shovel, and iron pry bar
Mixing box and masonry hoe
Forming lumber, mason's line, heavy work gloves, rake or board, pea gravel, brush, and wood block

---

REPLACEMENT

1. Break up the area to be replaced with a sledgehammer or pick. If the problem is a pavement section that has been uplifted by tree roots and cannot be simply relaid, break enough concrete off the corner to make a large notch to permit releveling of the section.

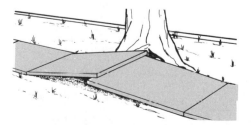

2. Relevel the gravel base if it has sunk; use the broken concrete as filler.

3. Brush the edges of the remaining concrete and wash with Concrete and Asphalt Cleaner to remove any organic refuse that might interfere with the repair's bond.

4. Apply the Concrete Bonding Adhesive to all exposed edges of the old concrete. Erect temporary forms along the edges.

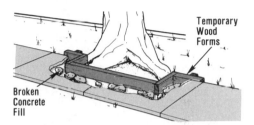

Temporary Wood Forms

Broken Concrete Fill

5. Place the concrete and cure with QUIKRETE® Acrylic Concrete Cure & Seal. For more information on curing and finishing the concrete, refer to page 2.

For Best Results

Use QUIKRETE® Fiber-Reinforced Concrete to eliminate damage caused by impacts or slight slab shifting or settling.

When QUIKRETE® Concrete Mix is used, reinforcement can be added.

Where a notch has been cut out around a tree trunk, sink a border of treated 2 × 4s flush with the grade. They can also be used as forms for placing the concrete.

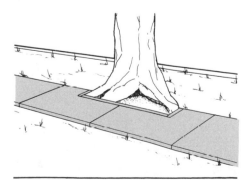

REPOSITIONING

Walks can shift, settle, and heave due to changes in the subgrade or pressure from tree roots. If the walk was built correctly, this cracking and movement should occur only at control and expansion joints, with complete sections of the walk remaining intact. In this case, the best repair method is to reposition the slab sections on a new base. If there is no cracking at the control joints, a chisel and small sledgehammer can be used to break the walk cleanly at these points. Wear heavy work gloves and be careful not to pinch your fingers or toes under the slab edge; the job will be easier if you have a helper.

1. Determine the desired finished height for the repositioned sections. String a mason's line at this height to give yourself a visual reference.

2. Use a long iron pry bar and small block of wood for lifting leverage. Never rest the pry bar directly on the adjacent concrete slab; the edge may chip or crumble under the pressure.

3. Use pieces of brick or flat stones to shim the slab to the correct level. Push them in place with a rake or board. Never put your arm beneath the raised slab. To allow for settlement, shim to a height slightly higher than required.

4. Once the slab is firmly supported on the bricks or stones, fill the voids beneath the slab with pea gravel.

Repairing Leaks in Concrete and Masonry

Despite the best construction methods, any concrete construction can eventually develop cracks through which moisture can leak, leading to further deterioration of the structure. If the cracks are in a water-holding vessel, such as a swimming pool, cistern, or fountain, they might not only be unsightly and a source of deterioration, they can also interfere with the efficiency or use of the structure. Follow these simple steps now to avoid drastic measures later.

Tools and Materials

QUIKRETE® Hydraulic Water-Stop Cement
QUIKRETE® Heavy-Duty Masonry Coating
QUIKRETE® Masonry Coating
QUIK-COAT™ Waterproofing Paint for Masonry
Pail, wooden paddle, and trowel
Hammer, chisel, wire brush, scraper, and hose

REPAIRING THE LEAKS

1. If the cracks are in a water-holding vessel, drain the water or wait until it is at a low enough level for the repairs to be done safely.

2. With a hammer and chisel, enlarge all cracks and holes. Cut squarely or un-

  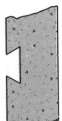

Wrong   Good   Best

dercut; do not make tapered, V-shaped cuts. The cavities should be enlarged to at least 3/4″ deep and 3/4″ wide.

3. Remove all loose material from the cavities, then scrub them out with a wire brush and water.

4. With a pail, a wooden paddle, and water, prepare only as much QUIKRETE® Hydraulic Water-Stop Cement as you can apply in a 3-minute period. Roll the mixed amount in your hands until you feel it begin to stiffen and become warm. (Be sure to wear gloves when handling this product.)

5. Beginning at the top, press the cement into the cavity with your fingers. Maintain pressure for a few minutes or until the cement sets and the leak stops.

6. Smooth the surface with water and a trowel. Keep the area moist for at least 15 minutes. When all cracks and holes have been repaired, waterproof the entire wall with QUIKRETE® Heavy-Duty Masonry Coating, QUIKRETE® Masonry Coating, or QUIK-COAT™ Waterproofing Paint for Masonry (see the following section).

Damp-proofing Concrete and Masonry

Whether new or old, concrete and masonry walls and structures, particularly

basements, should be treated with a water-resistant coating to prevent the entry of water and moisture that will lead to deterioration and damage.

The QUIKRETE® line of water-resistant products includes QUIKRETE® Masonry Coating, Heavy-Duty Masonry Coating, and QUIK-COAT™ Waterproofing Paint for Masonry. All three of these products are formulated for use on all interior and exterior walls, either above or below grade. These products are not for use on floors.

QUIKRETE® Masonry Coating and Heavy-Duty Masonry Coating are portland cement-based products that are mixed with water to a brushable consistency and applied. QUIKRETE® Heavy-Duty Masonry Coating is reinforced with minerals to provide the most durable water-resistant coating possible. QUIKRETE® QUIK-COAT™ Waterproofing Paint for Masonry is ready to apply from the can with a brush, roller, or spray equipment.

BASEMENT WALLS

Tools and Materials

QUIKRETE® Heavy-Duty Masonry Coating, QUIKRETE® Masonry Coating, or QUIKRETE® QUIKCOAT™ Waterproofing Paint for Masonry
QUIKRETE® Concrete and Asphalt Cleaner
QUIKRETE® Hydraulic Water-Stop Cement (as needed)
Large mixing vessel, heavy-duty masonry brush, wooden stirring paddle, wire brush, scraper, hose with spray nozzle, and paint roller or spray equipment (optional)
Household bleach or muriatic acid (as needed)

Damp basement walls can be caused by either condensation on the inside or water penetrating through the wall from the outside. To see if condensation is the problem, tape a 1′-square piece of aluminum foil to the wall with all four sides of the foil airtight. Keep the foil on the wall for 2 days, then remove and examine it. If the outside of the foil is moist, the problem is condensation. This can be corrected by installing a dehumidifier or by increasing the ventilation in the basement. If, on the other hand, the foil that was facing the wall is wet, the problem is water penetration.

Locating and Repairing Leaks

1. Inspect the walls to locate the source of the leak. Sources might include downspout gutters and soffits that are directing water against the wall from the outside. Shut off or redirect the water flow away from the wall, if possible.

2. Large cracks and leaks in the wall must be repaired before the coating or paint is applied. Use QUIKRETE® Hydraulic Water-Stop Cement to make the repairs. For details, see the preceding section, *Repairing Leaks in Concrete and Masonry*. Cure for several days before coating or painting.

QUIKRETE® MASONRY COATINGS

Proper surface preparation is very important before applying QUIKRETE® Heavy-Duty or standard Masonry Coatings.

1. If the surface is new, scrub it with a wire brush and rinse it with water. If the surface is especially smooth (poured concrete, for example), etch the surface with a 20% to 25% solution of muriatic acid, then rinse, or add QUIKRETE® Concrete Acrylic Fortifier to the mix water as outlined in Step 4.

2. If the masonry surface is old or if it has been covered with paint or some other coating, it must be cleaned thoroughly before applying the QUIKRETE® Masonry Coating. Remove all loose mortar, dirt, and paint with a wire brush or scraper. **At least 75%** of the original masonry surface should be exposed. Scrub dirty walls with a wire brush and QUIKRETE® Concrete & Asphalt Cleaner and rinse thoroughly.

3. Mix QUIKRETE® Heavy-Duty Masonry Coating in a clean, large container, using clean, cold water. Add approximately 1-1/2 gallons of water for every 40-pound bag of QUIKRETE® Heavy-Duty Masonry Coating, or 1 to 1-1/2 gallons of water for every 20-pound pail of QUIKRETE® Masonry Coating.

4. When applying over smooth, nonporous surfaces, QUIKRETE® Concrete Acrylic Fortifier should be used

as part of the mix liquid. Substitute 2 quarts of fortifier for 2 quarts of water in both Heavy-Duty and standard Masonry Coating mixes.

5. The mix will thin out slowly, so do not be tempted to add more water to the mix. Mix only enough material that can be applied in 2 hours.

6. Allow the mix to set for 20 minutes before application. Stir thoroughly just before beginning work and frequently as work proceeds.

7. Dampen the surface of porous walls before application. Wetting of smooth nonporous surfaces is not recommended.

8. Use a coarse fiber brush about 6″ in width to apply the coating to the wall. Scrub on the paint with a firm circular motion.

9. During hot, dry weather, fog spray the coating several times to prevent rapid setting.

10. Two coats of QUIKRETE® Masonry Coating are recommended. The second coat should be applied 12 to 48 hours after the first. Fog spray the first coat before applying the second coat. DO NOT fog spray or wet down the final coat after application.

For Best Results

Add mix to the water; don't add water to the mix.

To maintain color uniformity, use the same amount of QUIKRETE® Concrete Acrylic Fortifier in each batch of QUIKRETE® Masonry Coating.

Do not use too much mix water, or the material will thin out too much.

QUIKRETE® QUIK-COAT™ Waterproofing Paint for Masonry

QUIK-COAT™ Waterproofing Paint requires no premixing or prewetting of surfaces. It can be applied over uncured concrete and on slightly damp surfaces. However, best results are obtained when applied on dry walls and surfaces.

1. Clean the surface of all dirt, dust, grease, oil, and paint. Efflorescence can be removed using diluted household bleach or weak muriatic acid.

2. Patch all holes and cracks in the surface using QUIKRETE® Hydraulic Water-Stop Cement.

3. Thoroughly stir QUIK-COAT™ before application with a brush, heavy-nap roller, or paint spraying equipment. Do not add thinner to QUIK-COAT™. The best waterproofing results are obtained when applied with a heavy-duty masonry brush working the paint into the pores of the surface.

4. Porous masonry surfaces require two coats.

5. If excessive leaking is present, apply the first coat of QUIK-COAT™ to those areas and allow to dry overnight.

6. Apply the second coat to the entire surface. If leaking is still present, paint area again when previous coat is completely dry.

For Best Results

Apply only when temperature is above 50° F.

Use only in well-ventilated areas.

Restoring Concrete and Masonry Walls with QUIK-WALL® Surface Bonding Cement

QUIKWALL® Surface Bonding Cement adds strength, durability, and water resistance to walls made of concrete, concrete or cinder block, brick, terra cotta tile, and stone. It is an ideal material for restoring and/or beautifying buildings, walls, and chimneys. QUIKWALL® Surface Bonding Cement is also an excellent coating material for cisterns and other concrete water holding tanks. It can be used to repair silos and other farm buildings.

QUIKWALL® Surface Bonding Cement can be applied over porous and nonporous (smooth) concrete and masonry walls. However, when applying over smooth surfaces. QUIKRETE® Concrete Acrylic Fortifier must be used as part of the mix water.

Tools and Materials

QUIKWALL® Surface Bonding Cement
QUIKRETE® Concrete Acrylic Fortifier (nonporous surfaces)
QUIKRETE® Hydraulic Water-Stop Cement (as needed)
QUIKRETE® Masonry Coating (as needed)
Mixing equipment, trowel, hose with spray nozzle or large sponge, and brush

---

BUILDINGS

QUIKWALL® Surface Bonding Cement is very effective in restoring older buildings whose walls have begun to crack and loosen from the effects of time. A 1/8″ coating of QUIKWALL® SBC on the outside of the walls makes them practically impermeable to cold air drafts, so it is particularly suited for the renovation of horse barns and other farm buildings.

1. Clean all walls thoroughly to remove all paint, oil, dirt, and other foreign matter that can interfere with the bonding of QUIKWALL® Surface Bonding Cement.

2. Mix the QUIKWALL® SBC using 1-1/4 to 1-1/2 gallons of clean water to each 50-pound bag of material. Always add the powder to the water. If a power mixer is used, do not mix for more than 3 minutes.

Note: If the QUIKWALL® SBC is being applied to a nonporous surface, such as smooth concrete, brick, or terra cotta tile, substitute QUIKRETE® Concrete Acrylic Fortifier as part of the mix liquid.

Add 1/2 gallon of fortifier per 50-pound bag of Surface Bonding Cement.

3. On porous walls, wet the wall surface with a fine spray mist or use a heavy sponge to dampen the surface prior to applying the QUIKWALL® SBC.

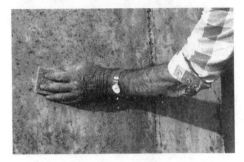

4. Load the finishing trowel with a good amount of mix.

5. Apply a 1/8″ thick coating of QUIKWALL® SBC to the wall. Work from bottom to top, using an upward sweeping motion.

6. Push the material into any cracks and broken areas of the wall. Texture-swirl the material as you apply it. Do not wait to give the QUIKWALL® SBC its final finish.

7. Moist-cure the walls after 8 hours by dampening them with a fine spray. Repeat several times daily for 3 days.

CISTERNS, HOLDING PONDS, AND OTHER WATER-HOLDING TANKS

Because QUIKWALL® SBC is highly water-resistant, it can be used as a lining on cisterns, holding ponds, and other water-holding tanks to prevent water loss. It is approved for use with potable water, so it's perfectly safe for both humans and animals. Be sure the surface is completely clean and dry before beginning the application, then apply the QUIKWALL® SBC as described earlier. When the QUIKWALL® SBC has completely dried, brush on a coat of QUIKRETE® Masonry Coating.

Note: If large cracks exist on the walls of the structure, it is recommended to first patch them with QUIKRETE® Hydraulic Water-Stop Cement. (For details, see *Repairing Leaks in Concrete and Masonry* section, page 130.) When the cement has dried completely, begin applying QUIKWALL® SBC over the entire surface.

SILOS

QUIKWALL® SBC provides the best protection against the acid that commonly forms in silos. Keep in mind that for the QUIKWALL® SBC to bond well, surface preparation is especially important in this application.

1. Clean the interior walls of the silo to remove the accumulated acid crust.

2. Remove the remaining traces of acid by washing the walls with lime water, then go over them again with plain water. Allow them to dry completely before beginning the QUIKWALL® SBC

application. If the silo walls are smooth and nonporous, use QUIK-RETE® Concrete Acrylic Fortifier as part of the mix water.

3. Apply the QUIKWALL® SBC in the same manner as described earlier. When relining silos, it is very important that the walls be troweled extra smooth to minimize the occurrence of small pockets where future acid crusting could originate.

CHIMNEYS

Without a doubt, chimneys must withstand a great deal of abuse from the elements. And while tuck-pointing repairs helps restore them to good condition, the improvement is only temporary. To do a job that will last, coat the entire part of the chimney that extends above the roof with an 1/8″ coating of QUIKWALL® SBC. Its high strength and water-resistant properties are ideal for combating wind, rain, ice, and snow.

For Best Results

Machine mix if at all possible.

Do not apply QUIKWALL® Surface Bonding Cement if temperatures will exceed 100°F or fall below 40°F within a 24 hour period.

Do not add winter admixtures or other additives to the mix, except QUIK-RETE® Concrete Acrylic Fortifier when needed.

Do not allow premature drying of the coating, which can lead to cracking and other failures. Cure properly.

Repairing with Quick-Setting Cement

Many homeowners neglect repairs to precast pieces, chipped concrete statuary, and even angled concrete (such as steps and corners) out of a lack of confidence in their abilities to work with concrete, or a feeling that the repairs are not worth the effort of making suitable forms. QUIKRETE® Quick-Setting Cement makes these and similar jobs simple enough for even the inexperienced do-it-yourselfer to achieve more than satisfactory results. Specially formulated for use where rapid setting and high strengths are needed, it sets in 5 to 10 minutes and can be sculpted with a trowel to match the surrounding surface without any lengthy delays. No forms are needed. It just might take more patience and know-how to bring in a Georgia catfish.

3. If the damage is less than 1″ deep, mix QUIKRETE® Concrete Acrylic Fortifier as the mix liquid to strengthen the cement. If the damage is deeper than 1″, use clean water instead of liquid fortifier.

4. Mix 5-1/2 parts QUIKRETE® Quick-Setting Cement to 1 part liquid. Mix until smooth and prepare only as much cement as can be applied in 5 minutes.

Tools and Materials

QUIKRETE® Quick-Setting Cement
QUIKRETE® Concrete Acrylic Fortifier
Pointing trowel or bricklayer's trowel
Hammer, chisel, safety glasses, and
  brush

REPAIRS

1. Undercut and/or square the edges of the damaged area with a hammer and chisel. Be sure to wear safety glasses to prevent injury from flying chips of concrete.

2. Brush all loose material and dirt from the area to be repaired. Dampen the damaged surface.

5. Apply the cement to the damaged surface, rough-shaping it to the proper contours as it is applied.

6. The cement will take its initial set in 5 to 10 minutes. After this time it will retain a firm thumbprint. At this point it can be shaved and sculpted with the edge of a trowel.

For Best Results

Keep the repair moist for 24 hours. Cover with plastic film to retain moisture.

Skid-proofing Concrete Surfaces

Combine QUIKRETE® Sand Mix and QUIKRETE® Concrete Acrylic Fortifier to create a nonskid surface around pools, walks, and boat docks.

Tools and Materials

QUIKRETE® Sand Mix
QUIKRETE® Concrete Acrylic Fortifier
Masking tape, trowel, brush or broom, hoe, and mixing box

APPLICATION

1. Lay masking tape around the edges of the surface to be coated. Make certain that the surface is clean and free of dust, dirt, and loose matter.

2. Mix 1-2/3 quarts of fortifier with 60 pounds of Sand Mix; for larger and smaller mixtures refer to the directions on the back of the fortifier bottle. Add water to achieve the desired consistency.

3. Trowel the mix onto the surface in a minimum 1/4″-thick coat.

4. Brush the mix to achieve a rough texture.

For Best Results

Acrylic paint can be added to the wet mix before application if a particular color is desired.

Sealing around Pipes

The cut-out openings around
basement pipes are prime areas for
moisture to enter your home, not to
mention insects and vermin. To keep
these unwelcome visitors out of your
home, seal around all pipes with
QUIKRETE® Hydraulic Water-Stop
Cement or QUIKRETE® Quick-Setting
Cement. They are specially formulated
so they can be sculpted to fit securely
around pipes for an effective,
watertight seal.

SEALING

1. Square the edges of the hole with a
   hammer and chisel.

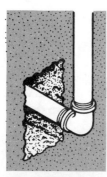

2. Be sure the edges of the hole are
   free of dirt and other loose material,
   then dampen the area slightly.
3. Mix the QUIKRETE® Hydraulic
   Water-Stop Cement and make the
   initial application with a mason's
   trowel, filling in the hole generously.
4. After the initial set, work the patch
   with the edge of the trowel to firm
   up the cement around the pipe.

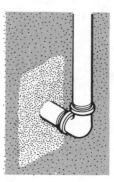

Note: If your basement is warm and
dry, it is best to keep the patch moist
for 24 hours by covering it with
polyethylene film.

Tuck-Pointing Mortar Joints/ Replacing Damaged Brick

The cutting out and repointing of
mortar joints in brick, block, and stone
masonry is one of the most common
repairs performed by masons. Left
unrepaired, water can seep in between
the cracked, loose mortar and cause
interior wall damage.

Tools and Materials

QUIKRETE® Mortar Mix or Mason Mix, or QUIKRETE® Vinyl Concrete Patcher, or QUIKRETE® Hydraulic Water-Stop Cement

Plugging or joint chisel, bricklayer's hammer, wire brush or bristle brush, garden hose, jointer, pointing trowel, and wheelbarrow or mortarboard

MIXING THE MORTAR OR MASON MIX

While QUIKRETE® Mortar Mix or Mason Mix is the product of choice for most applications, especially larger jobs, other QUIKRETE® products also give excellent repointing results. If you plan to make a number of concrete repairs such as filling cracks, repairing chipped edges, resurfacing scaled areas, as well as doing some repointing, QUIKRETE® Vinyl Concrete Patcher can handle all these jobs. And if you plan to patch leaks in block or brick walls with QUIKRETE® Hydraulic Water-Stop Cement, repoint the surrounding joints as well. Always follow the directions listed on the individual product package.

When using QUIKRETE® Mortar Mix or Mason Mix for repointing, it is recommended that you prehydrate the mortar prior to tuck-pointing joints. This step will greatly reduce the shrinkage of any of the joints away from the edge of the bricks and cut down on the number of hairline cracks that occur when the mortar begins to dry against the old bricks.

To prehydrate the mortar, mix the required amount of QUIKRETE® Mortar Mix or Mason Mix with just enough water to form a damp unworkable mix that retains its form when pressed into a ball in the hand. Let the mortar set for about 30 to 45 minutes, and then add enough water to make the mortar workable. The end result will be a mix slightly drier than that normally used to lay new brick. Never make large batches of mortar for repointing; mix an amount you can use in about 45 minutes.

PREPARING THE JOINTS

1. Cut out the mortar joints to an approximate depth of 3/4″ to 1″. Use of the special plugging or joint chisel will help prevent binding in the joint and chipping of the brick edges.

2. A clean surface is needed for good bonding. Use the jointer tool to rake

out excess mortar or grit, and brush out the joints to remove loose mortar or sand.

3. Flush out any remaining particles with a garden hose equipped with a spray attachment.

REPLACING BAD BRICKS

Any bricks in the wall that are badly broken or deteriorated should be cut out and replaced prior to repointing. Select new bricks that match the old bricks as closely as possible.

1. Cut the old brick completely out of the wall.

2. Clean out the recess carefully.

3. Wet the cavity and the replacement unit with a brush or fine spray of water. When the cavity is damp, but not wet, apply a thick layer of QUIK-RETE® Mortar Mix or Mason Mix to the bottom and sides of the cavity.

4. Butter the top of the replacement brick and slide it into the cavity. Mortar should squeeze out from the joints. If it does not, rebutter the joint, adding more mortar.

REPOINTING

1. Dampen the cleaned joints with a brush and water.

2. Load the trowel with mortar. Pick up the mortar from the trowel with the jointer tools and press it into the joints. Pack the mortar firmly into the joints. Repoint the head joints first and the bed joints second. This sequence allows you to make unbroken horizontal strokes with the jointer to form straight, even bed joints.

3. In most cases, joints are filled flush to the wall face, then slightly depressed with the jointer and brushed clean. If concave or V joints were used in the original work, strike with the proper tool for these finishes after the repointing is done and before the mortar gets too hard to work.

4. To decrease the possibility of cracking or sagging in extremely deep joints, fill in about half of the joint depth, wait until the mortar is thumbprint hard, and then repoint the remainder of the joint.

5. In hot or windy conditions, dampen the repointed joints to prevent the mortar from drying too fast. Spray the finished job with a fine water mist to aid in the curing process.

6. Repointing of stonework and block is essentially the same as brickwork. Tool the joints to match those in the sound sections of the wall.

Repairing Chimneys

Although repairing a leaning chimney or one that is leaking smoke through the brick joints are jobs best left to a professional, there are some important repairs that anyone can perform. These include repairs to preserve the integrity of the brickwork and to avoid more serious and expensive work in the future. If your chimney has crumbling pointing or holes and cracks in the cap, doing the repairs yourself immediately will prevent further weakening and avoid the costly job of rebuilding or replacing it later. Getting up to the chimney might require some time and effort because scaffolding is usually necessary, but the repairs themselves are straightforward tasks.

REPOINTING A CHIMNEY

Repointing a chimney does not require a great deal of mortar. QUIKRETE® Mor-

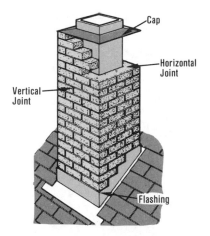

loose brick, then lift it out. Scrape all loose or crumbling mortar from the hole.

8. After cleaning the brick of any mortar and dirt, dampen the brick as well as those surrounding the cavity. Butter its top, bottom, and both ends and press it back into the opening. Make sure the joints are completely filled and strike them flat.

For Best Results

When working on or around any part of a chimney, be sure to close all dampers leading into it so if any soot is knocked loose it will not enter the house.

tar Mix or Mason Mix is available in bags conveniently sized to provide just enough mortar for the present job or to have a little left over for other small jobs. QUIK-RETE® Vinyl Concrete Patcher can be used instead for better adhesion.

Tools and Materials

QUIKRETE® Mortar Mix or Mason Mix or QUIKRETE® Vinyl Concrete Patcher
Mason's 2lb. hammer, 3/8″ chisel, brush, brick trowel, and mortarboard
Scaffolding, heavy gloves, and safety glasses or goggles

CLEANING AND REPOINTING

1. Hold the chisel at a sharp angle to the joint while striking it with a hammer and knock out the crumbling joints to a depth of at least 1/2″. Work the chisel along the joint about 1″ at a time.

2. Chip out vertical joints first, then do horizontal joints.

3. Brush any loose particles of dirt or mortar out of the joints.

4. Dampen the joints.

5. Prepare as much mortar as can be used in 1 hour and trowel it into the vertical joints first, then the horizontal joints. Strike the joints flat.

6. After the mortar hardens, brush off any excess.

7. In the course of repointing, you might come across a loose brick or two that should be replaced. Use the chisel to remove the mortar from around the

REPAIRING THE CAP

1. Brush out any loose particles, dirt, and organic matter from cracks and holes in the cap.

2. Dampen the crack or hole and trowel in fresh mortar to fill it flush with the surrounding surface. QUIKRETE® Vinyl Concrete Patcher can be used to fill any cracks between the cap and the flue liner.

3. The cap should be replaced only if it is badly cracked or if the mortar is so loose that it is pulling away from the brickwork. Use the hammer and chisel to chip the cap away in pieces. For safety, lower the pieces in a bucket instead of just letting them fly off the roof.

4. Brush away all dirt and loose particles.

5. Trowel on the fresh mortar in several thick layers, sloping the cap down from the flue liner to the outside edges of the chimney stack.

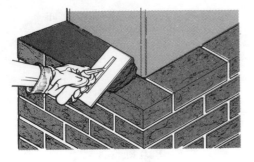

For Best Results

Use safety glasses or goggles and gloves if the repairs are going to require extensive concrete chipping. Eye injuries and scaffolding work can be a very dangerous combination.

FLASHING REPAIR

Chimney flashing should be inspected if there are interior water stains in the area of the chimney. If the flashing is loose, simple repointing is needed; if the flashing has deteriorated, it will have to be replaced.

Tools and Materials

QUIKRETE® Mortar Mix or Mason Mix
Joint raker, brush, pointing trowel,
   and slicker jointer

REPOINTING FLASHING

1. Rake out loose and crumbling mortar from the joints where the flashing and chimney stack meet.
2. Brush any loose particles and dust out of the joint.
3. Dampen the interior of the joint and any remaining mortar. Pack fresh mortar into the joint with the pointing trowel.
4. After the mortar has set slightly, strike the joint flat with the slicker.

For Best Results

If both vertical and horizontal joints have to be repointed around the flashing, repoint the vertical joints first.

Repairing Sunken Brick or Stone Walks/ Patios

Repairing stone or brick paving that has sunk is a task even the novice do-it-yourselfer can perform to restore both safety and attractiveness. But before beginning, try to determine the cause of the damage and remove it to avoid repeating your efforts. If water erosion has undermined the base (such as from a gutter downspout), first try removing the source or redirecting the flow. Installing a bed of gravel or a concrete base beneath the pavement and setting the pavers in a wet mortar mixture will also increase the permanence of the repairs. For more information on paving bases, refer to *Patios, Walkways, and Driveways* (page 94).

MORTARLESS PAVING

If the cause of the sinking is only ground settlement over the years, these repairs can most likely be done with only minimal time, effort, and money. If the cause is more serious, a different paving method might be called for.

Tools and Materials

QUIKRETE® All-Purpose Sand
Carpenter's level or a straight length
   of 2 × 4
Shovel and broom

REPAIRS

1. Remove any loose, broken, or sunken pavers. If your examination shows that adjacent pavers have not been displaced, but that settlement has occurred beneath them as well—so that they are not sitting squarely on the base—they should also be removed.

2. Fill the depression with QUIKRETE® All-Purpose Sand up to the level of the surrounding base.

3. Set the pavers back into place. Check their level with the surrounding pavement with the carpenter's level or 2 × 4. If the pavers are not level, tap them gently to seat them. Replace any broken pavers.

4. Spread All-Purpose Sand over the repaired area and sweep it into the joints. Dampen the sand with a fine spray; repeat until the joints are completely filled.

For Best Results

For greater strength, dry QUIKRETE® Mortar Mix or Mason Mix can be substituted for the joint sand. Follow the same repair procedures.

MORTARED PAVING

Mortared joints and a concrete base make sinking infrequent in mortared paving, but when it does occur it usually indicates a more serious problem than just ground settlement. Before making the repairs after the sunken pavers are removed, check and correct any problems with area drainage.

Tools and Materials

QUIKRETE® Mortar Mix or Mason Mix
QUIKRETE® Sand Mix or Concrete Mix (if necessary)
QUIKRETE® Concrete Bonding Adhesive (if necessary)
Mason's hammer, joint chisel or cold chisel, trowel, jointer, hoe, hawk, and mixing box
Shovel, sledgehammer, float, and wire mesh reinforcing (if necessary)

REPAIRS

1. With the hammer and chisel remove the pavers in the sunken area. Do this as carefully as possible to avoid breaking the pavers.

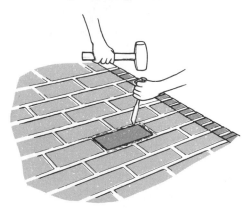

2. Examine the slab base for breakage. If there is major damage, that section of the slab should be removed with the sledgehammer and replaced with fresh concrete. Before placing the

new concrete, track down and correct the cause of the problem. For more details on placing the new concrete, refer to *Repairing Concrete Walks* (page 129). If the cause of the sinkage cannot be corrected, use the wire mesh to reinforce the concrete.

3. If the damage or sinking of the slab is relatively minor, use sand mix to bring the area back to the level of the surrounding concrete. Be sure to clean the original slab of any dirt, dust, soil, and organic matter before placing the sand mix. After it is placed, float it and allow it to cure for 3 to 4 days before replacing the paving.

REPLACING PAVING

1. Chip all the old mortar from the pavers with the hammer and chisel. Brush the bed and head joints clean of any loose flakes or dust.

2. Lay in a 1/2" mortar bed on the concrete slab.

3. Begin laying the pavers from an outside corner of the damaged area using the same size joints as in the original paving. Butter the head joints of each paver before placing it. Replace any broken pavers.

4. Strike the tops of the joints flat to prevent water entry. After the mortar is dry enough to be brushed without smearing, brush away any loose particles of mortar.

For Best Results

Clean all surfaces to be bonded with QUIKRETE® Concrete & Asphalt Cleaner before applying the concrete or mortar mixes.

Sealing Concrete and Masonry

QUIKRETE® Acrylic Concrete Cure & Seal forms a tough, water-resistant finish that is virtually unaffected by exposure to

water, common acids, alkalies, petroleum solvents, oils, greases, and salts. QUIK-RETE® Acrylic Concrete Cure & Seal quickly penetrates the surface of concrete, flagstone, or unglazed tile to harden, protect, and preserve the material. Use it to seal walks, driveways, garage floors, concrete porch decks, steps, patios, exposed aggregate finishes, and any other concrete surface exposed to weather and harsh environments.

Tools and Materials

QUIKRETE® Acrylic Concrete
  Cure & Seal
QUIKRETE® Concrete & Asphalt
  Cleaner
Scrub brush, broom, paintbrush,
  roller, mop or squeegee, and clean
  container

SURFACE PREPARATION

1. Remove all wax, oil, grease, dirt, and dust from the surface to be sealed. Use QUIKRETE® Concrete & Asphalt Cleaner, as needed.

2. Allow the surface to dry completely before applying sealer.

APPLICATION

1. Pour the QUIKRETE® Acrylic Concrete Cure & Seal slowly into a clean container. Stir gently but thoroughly to mix. Rigorous stirring can form air bubbles in the sealer, which could affect the final finish.

2. Apply a small amount of sealer to an inconspicuous area to ensure aesthetic compatibility.

3. Apply to the dry surface full strength, using a brush, roller, mop, or squeegee.

4. In most cases, one coat provides sufficient protection. Very porous surfaces may require two coats. Allow to dry 2 hours between coats.

For Best Results

Do not apply at temperatures below 40° F.

Do not apply if rain is likely.

Never thin QUIKRETE® Acrylic Concrete Cure & Seal with water solvents.

Repairing Blacktop

Repairs to blacktop, asphalt, or macadam driveways, tennis and basketball courts, and similar constructions are repairs you can easily do yourself with QUIKRETE® products, whether the problem is a slight crack or a more troublesome chuckhole.

CHUCKHOLE PATCHING

QUIKRETE® Blacktop Patch is designed and manufactured to repair even large chuckholes with a firm and durable patch without mixing or heating. Use it just as it comes in the bag.

Tools and Materials

QUIKRETE® Blacktop Patch
TRAFFIC TOP® Driveway Sealer
Chisel, handpick, or circular saw,
  small broom or brush, and tamper

PATCHING THE HOLE

1. Chisel or cut the edges of the hole straight down to a depth of at least 1″; square off the hole as much as possible.

2. Sweep all loose material out of the hole.

3. Place the Blacktop Patch in 1/2″ layers, tamping each layer solid.

4. Final compaction may be done by covering the patch with a piece of plastic or plywood and driving over it with a car.

5. Wait at least 1 month before sealing the entire driveway with QUIKRETE® TRAFFIC TOP® Driveway Sealer.

Note: Blacktop Patch is designed to patch potholes or large cracks. It is not intended for paving.

For Best Results

Keep the Blacktop Patch in a warm location until it is ready to be used. Do not use it if the temperature is below 50°F.

Sprinkle dry sand or cement on the surface of the patch to speed curing and to remove adhesiveness of the patch's surface.

Do not use Blacktop Patch when rain is expected within a few hours.

Allow the patch to cure for 1-1/2 days before driving over it.

CRACK REPAIRS

QUIKRETE® Latex Blacktop Crack Seal comes in handy 1-quart bottles to make repairs as easy as possible. It is designed to fill cracks in blacktop up to 1/2″ in width.

Tools and Materials

QUIKRETE® Latex Blacktop Crack Seal
QUIKRETE® All-Purpose Sand (as needed)

REPAIRING THE CRACK

1. Remove all loose dirt, soil, and organic matter from the crack.

2. Shake the bottle well before cutting the tip. Pour the Crack Seal into the crack, overfilling slightly to allow for shrinkage. Do not apply more then 1/4″ thick in a single application.

3. For deep cracks, sprinkle clean sand into the crack within 1/4″ of the surface before applying the Crack Seal.

For Best Results

Apply the Crack Seal only when the outside air temperature is between 50° and 100°F.

Do not use if rain is likely within 24 hours.

Do not apply in cracks wider then 1/2″.

QUIKRETE® Blacktop Repair Caulk is also ideal for repairing cracks in blacktop. It dries to a more textured finish and is particularly ideal for inclined or vertical surfaces.

Repairing Stucco

One of stucco's advantages as siding is that it rarely needs repairs, and when it does need repairs they are usually simple. However, if the area to be repaired is more than 2 square feet, the stucco should be removed all the way down to the wall surface and built up as described in the earlier section on stuccoing. For more common repairs, including cracks, read on.

Tools and Materials

QUIKRETE® Finish-Coat Stucco
QUIKRETE® Concrete Acrylic Fortifier
Hammer, cold chisel, knife, wire
  brush, and trowel

REPAIRS

1. Remove loose stucco from the damaged area.

2. Use the hammer and chisel or knife to undercut the stucco surrounding the damaged area so that the patch will be locked in.

3. Use the wire brush to remove any stucco knocked loose in undercutting. Brush the entire damaged area free of dirt, dust, and other foreign materials.

4. Thoroughly wet down the damaged area and keep it damp for 12 hours

before patching to prevent the moisture from being drawn too quickly from the patch and weakening it.

5. Mix QUIKRETE® Finish-Coat Stucco with QUIKRETE® Concrete Acrylic Fortifier. Tightly pack the prepared stucco finish into the damaged area with a trowel and texture it to match the surrounding stucco.

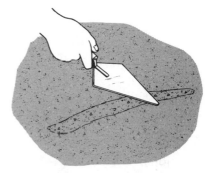

6. For deep repairs extending to the scratch coat, first tightly pack the hole within 1/4" of the surface. Keep the patch damp for 2 days while it sets.

7. Dampen the edges of the hole and the surface of the first layer; trowel in a second layer level with the original stucco and texture it to match.

Regrouting and Replacing Tile

Tools and Materials

QUIKRETE® Multi-Purpose Thin-Set
QUIKRETE® Polymer-Modified Tile
  Grout
Putty knife, toothbrush, hammer,
  straight bar or chisel, trowel, and
  plastic sheet

REGROUTING TILE

As grout gets older, it tends to chip away. This allows water to seep behind the tile and, eventually, it will loosen. When regrouting is necessary, proceed as follows:

1. With a putty knife, dig out the old grout. Remove all loose material, then dampen the joint.

2. Apply the new grout, working it into the joints with a toothbrush.

3. Smooth the grout with your finger. Be sure to clean off any excess from the tile immediately.

REPLACING TILE

In those cases where tile is damaged beyond repair, your only choice is to replace it. Use the following technique:

1. If only a few random tiles must be replaced, use a hammer to break them up. Remove all the pieces of tile and grout.

2. If you are replacing an entire section of tile, use a hammer and a straight bar or chisel to loosen the top tile. It should work free by tapping lightly with the hammer. Work down and remove the rest of the tile in the same manner.

3. Once the old tile has been removed, use the putty knife to completely remove the old adhesive. On larger areas, it is a good idea to sand the entire surface with a belt sander after scraping with the knife.

4. Apply the mortar and set the new tile. (see the *Tile Installation* section on page 98 for details.)

5. Wait a day or two for the mortar to set, then remove the spacers, dampen the joints, and apply the grout.

For Best Results

If you are working in a shower or bathtub enclosure, protect the tub by covering it with a sheet of plastic to prevent tile chips from scratching it.

When working around fixtures with a hammer and straight bar or chisel, be careful to avoid damaging the fixtures.

Repairing Drywall and Plaster

Holes and cracks in plaster and drywall are easily repairable. QUIKRETE® Patching Plaster in 3-pound pails and 25-pound bags makes the job even easier with its slow setting time, which allows more plaster to be mixed and worked at one time, and its virtually no-shrinkage formula. The plaster sets within 30 minutes.

Tools and Materials

QUIKRETE® Patching Plaster
Broad-edged putty knife, pocketknife or file, brush, plasterer's trowel (for larger repairs), and a sanding block

PATCHING CRACKS

1. Undercut the edges of each crack with the tang end of your file or pocketknife so that the inside opening is wider than the face.

2. Brush out the loose particles and dust.

3. Thoroughly dampen the edges using a brush or plant sprayer.

4. Use cross-hatched strokes with the putty knife to fill all voids in the crack with patching plaster.

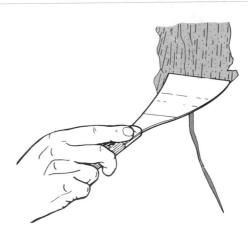

5. After filling each crack, immediately remove excess plaster from the wall.

6. After the patch has dried for several hours, sand it smooth with a fine-grade sandpaper.

For Best Results

Patching plaster should be applied in several layers for especially wide or deep cracks. Allow several hours drying time between layers.

Place a primer paint coat on the patch if it is to be painted.

PATCHING HOLES

1. Undercut around the edge of each hole with a sturdy knife or other sharp tool.

2. Chip away loose fragments.

3. Brush loose particles and dust from the hole; thoroughly dampen the backing and edge.

4. For holes in drywall without backing or holes that go all the way through the plaster, insert a piece of wire mesh with a piece of wire run through it.

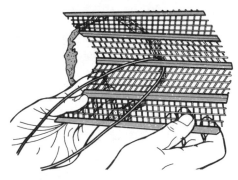

5. Tighten the wire around a pencil or similar object until the mesh is held firmly against the wall.

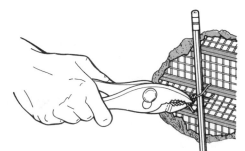

6. Use the putty knife to smooth the plaster into the hole, about halfway to the surface. If a wire mesh is being used, leave an opening for the pencil wire so that it can be removed after the plaster hardens.

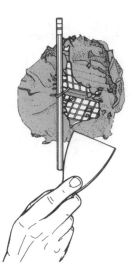

7. Rewet the first coat after it has hardened. Smooth on the second coat to a level just below the surface.

8. Rewet the second coat after hardening. Use a plasterer's trowel to achieve a smooth finish on the final coat; press heavily on the trowel to pack the final coat tightly.

9. After the final coat stiffens slightly, rewet the surface with a clean brush. Immediately retrowel, tipping the leading edge up slightly, while pressing heavily on the trailing edge; this will produce a shiny finish.

For Best Results

For smaller holes without backing— where a lighting fixture is removed, for example—rolled up paper can be used to fill the hole as a backer for the plaster instead of wire mesh.

Plaster Hardcoating

QUIKRETE® Patching Plaster can be used to create a smooth or slightly textured plaster hardcoat surface over dry-wall or sound plaster surfaces. Its 30-minute set time allows ample time to apply and finish plaster in larger batches. This reduces mixing time and minimizes the chance of slight color variations be-tween multiple batches.

Tools and Materials

QUIKRETE® Patching Plaster
Wide shallow mixing container
Plaster trowel or wide medium bristle
  paintbrush

SURFACE PREPARATION

Drywall must be installed, taped, and spackled using accepted drywall installa-tion techniques. The surface should be clean and free of dirt and dust. Old plas-ter surfaces should be in good condition with all holes and cracks properly patched with QUIKRETE® Patching Plas-ter as described on page 149.

MIXING AND APPLICATION

1. Mix only enough plaster that can com-fortably be applied in 20 to 25 min-utes. A large shallow mixing container is ideal since it gives plenty of room to load the trowel or brush.

2. Add water to the QUIKRETE® Patch-ing Plaster and mix thoroughly to a creamy, butter-like consistency. An overly stiff plaster mix will not apply smoothly.

3. Apply the plaster to the wall using a plaster trowel or a wide bristle brush. The trowel will create a smooth or slightly ridged surface, while the brush is ideal for forming swirled patterns.

4. Plaster thickness should be between 1/16" to 1/8". Texture or finish the plaster as soon as it is applied. Do not wet down the plaster after it is applied to the surface to soften it for finishing, and avoid multiple layers or thick tex-tured patterns. QUIKRETE® Patching Plaster is designed to impart a thin hardcoat finish.

For Best Results

Mix the plaster thoroughly to avoid lumps or dry spots in the mix.

Load the trowel or brush with a good amount of plaster and work at a good pace.

Practice your application and textur-ing technique on a test panel of dry-wall or inconspicuous area before be-ginning the main work.

Discard the plaster mix as soon as it shows signs of setting. Plaster that has begun to set will be difficult to apply to a thin coat and may lump up or stick to the trowel or brush.

Preparing Surfaces for Carpet, Resilient Flooring, and Tile

QUIKRETE® Fast-Set Underlayment and QUIKRETE® Self-Leveling Floor Resurfacer are used for repairing and leveling pitted and rough concrete or wood floors prior to installing carpeting, resilient flooring, or tile.

QUIKRETE® FAST-SET UNDERLAYMENT

QUIKRETE® Fast-Set Underlayment is a rapid-hardening, high-strength trowelable product that is hand applied to a thickness of 1/4″. It is ideal for spot repairs and leveling or for smaller surface preparation jobs. It can be applied to both concrete and wood surfaces.

Tools and Materials

QUIKRETE® Fast-Set Underlayment
QUIKRETE® Concrete and Asphalt Cleaner
Trowel, brush, and scrub brush

SURFACE PREPARATION

Remove all dirt, dust, and paint from the surfaces to be coated. Use QUIKRETE® Concrete and Asphalt Cleaner to remove grease and stubborn dirt from concrete surfaces.

MIXING AND APPLICATIONS

1. Mix using clean equipment and tools. The correct mix ratio is 3-1/2 pints of water to every 25-pound bag of QUIKRETE® Fast-Set Underlayment.

2. Be sure all material is thoroughly blended.

3. Do not mix more material than can be applied in 20 minutes.

4. Use a trowel to spread and smooth the underlayment material. It will set in approximately 30 minutes and may be walked on after that time. Setting time can be affected by using too much mixing water and/or the ambient working temperature. Cool conditions will slow setting time.

5. QUIKRETE® Fast-Set Underlayment should be allowed to air dry. No special curing steps are needed.

QUIKRETE® SELF-LEVELING FLOOR RESURFACER

QUIKRETE® Self-Leveling Floor Resurfacer is a self-leveling, self-finishing floor topping and underlayment specially formulated to work without troweling. This product is simply mixed to a pourable consistency, poured over the floor surface, and allowed to find its own level. It is ideal for leveling larger areas, and can be used over precast floor slabs, new concrete, weather damaged concrete, or finished concrete with rough or otherwise unacceptable surfaces. QUIKRETE® Self-Leveling Floor Resurfacer can even be installed over wood floor systems provided expanded metal lath is installed to the flooring.

QUIKRETE® Self-Leveling Floor Resurfacer can be installed to a maximum thickness of 5/8″ and will also level itself to a featheredge. Also, if the resurfacer is marred before it has gained its set, the material will self-heal itself. However, care should be taken to avoid marring the surface during application. Areas to receive QUIKRETE® Self-Leveling Floor Resurfacer must be protected from the sun or wind that can cause rapid loss of moisture. This could lead to incomplete hydration and potential cracking.

Tools and Materials

QUIKRETE® Self-Leveling Floor Resurfacer (Fast Set or Normal Set) and Primer
QUIKRETE® Concrete and Asphalt Cleaner
QUIKRETE® Sand Mix
QUIKRETE® Concrete Acrylic Fortifier
Mixing buckets, power drill with mixing paddle, wood or metal strips, trowel, scrub brush, large paintbrush, and duct tape or caulking
Expanded metal lath (only wood floors)

SURFACE PREPARATION

1. Clean the concrete slab or floor of all dirt, dust, oil, grease, paint, or water-soluble material. Use QUIKRETE® Concrete and Asphalt Cleaner for removing grease, oil, and stubborn dirt.

2. Fill any deep holes or depressions to existing floor elevation using a mix of QUIKRETE® Sand Mix and Concrete Acrylic Fortifier. Allow any repaired areas to cure completely before pouring the Floor Resurfacer.

3. Seal all perimeter openings, such as doorways, using strips of wood or metal. These dams should be able to retain resurfacer material at a height greater than the anticipated final floor height. Seal the outer wall to floor joint with duct tape or temporary caulking so that liquid Floor Resurfacer will not leak at the dam area.

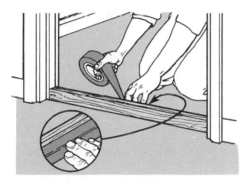

4. Prime the clean dry floor surface using a mix of 1 part QUIKRETE® Self-Leveling Primer to 4 parts water. Brush or spray this primer coat on the floor to produce a uniform coating with no pools or puddles. Apply 1 coat of diluted primer to new and precast concrete surfaces and 2 coats to old concrete surfaces.

5. Allow the primer to dry. This is normally 1 to 2 hours.

MIXING

1. Always add the QUIKRETE® Self-Leveling Floor Resurfacer powder to the mix water. DO NOT ADD WATER TO THE POWDER. Use the proper mix ratio stated on the package. Using too much water can cause separation, reduced strength, and shrinkage of the cured resurfacer.

2. Mix the resurfacer using a power drill equipped with a suitable mixing paddle. Hand mixing will not produce a smooth uniform mix. Mix for 4 minutes at 250 to 500 rpm.

PLACING

Place the liquid resurfacer by pouring it directly from the mixing container onto the floor surface. Placing should be done as one continuous operation with no major breaks between pours. The mixed compound remains fluid for approximately 20 minutes, so on larger jobs it is advisable to have someone mixing batches while others place them.

1. Work from wall to wall across the narrow width of the room. Pour the liquid resurfacer in continuous strips about 1' wide. Pour at a rate that allows the resurfacer to find its own level.

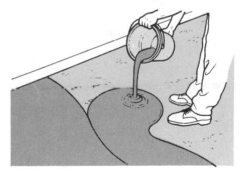

2. After waiting no more than 15 minutes, pour the second batch adjacent to the first batch. Continue to work without breaks until the entire floor surface is covered.

3. Do not walk on the resurfaced floor until it has fully gained sufficient strength. This is approximately 1 to 2 days for the Normal Set product or 2-4 hours for the Fast Set product, depending on surrounding conditions. No special curing steps are required.

4. When using the Normal Set product, wait 1 to 2 weeks before installing finished flooring over the resurfaced area. The Fast Set product can be covered in 24-48 hours.

For Best Results

Clean mixing tools immediately after use.

Mix thoroughly using mechanical means, and do not add too much water to the mix.

SECTION III: MATERIALS, TOOLS, AND PLANNING WITH QUIKRETE®

As you've seen in the previous sections, concrete, brick, block, stone, tile, stucco, and other cement-based wall coatings provide the beauty, durability, and versatility no other building material can match. When problems occur, repairs can be made with a minimum of time and effort. Anyone who can plan and work carefully using the basic tools and techniques discussed in this section can complete any of the projects and repairs illustrated earlier. This section introduces you to all of the QUIKRETE® products, a quality line that will take the guesswork and much of the labor out of masonry work.

QUIKRETE® concrete and mortar mixes

QUIKRETE® PRODUCT LINE

The QUIKRETE® line of masonry construction and repair products includes everything you'll need to successfully build and repair with concrete. The following product descriptions are intended as a guide to help you select the best QUIKRETE® product for your particular job.

QUIKRETE® Concrete and Mortar Mixes

One of the most problematic aspects of standard concrete and masonry work has always been selecting the proper ingredients and mixing them in correct proportions. Finding quality, clean, organic-free aggregates at convenient locations is sometimes difficult; and transporting, handling, and storing materials can be bothersome and expensive, especially for smaller jobs.

QUIKRETE® ready-to-use mixes solve the problem of correct proportioning and simplify your material selection, transportation, and storage problems. Every bag contains the correct blend of cement and clean aggregate for concrete or mortar. Just add water and mix as directed, and you're ready to begin work. Conveniently sized bags let you buy just the amount you need, so there's no concern about what to do with the extra sand or gravel piles often left when mixing from scratch. You're handling one product, not two or three. And with QUIKRETE®, quality is assured.

QUIKRETE® Concrete Mix. Concrete mix is used for any type of general concrete work, such as building walkways, patios, driveways, and all types of slab work. Concrete mix is also ideal for placing footers, foundations, steps, ramps, and walls. Uniform aggregate size makes mixing, placing, and finishing easier. A 60-pound bag covers approximately a half cubic foot; see page 189 for further information regarding yield.

QUIKRETE® Fiber-Reinforced Concrete Mix. This mix is the material of choice for slabs, steps, and cast projects 2" thick or more when chip and crack concerns are present. Special synthetic fibers added to the mix increase tensile strength and reduce cracking and chipping by over 50%. QUIKRETE® Fiber-Reinforced Concrete Mix also eliminates the need for wire mesh reinforcement in typical slab-on-grade applications. When properly placed and cured, compressive strength exceeds 4000 psi.

This easy to mix, place, and finish concrete is packaged in 60-pound bags. One bag yields a half cubic foot.

QUIKRETE® Fast-Setting Concrete Mix. This fast-setting mix sets wood or metal posts and poles in 20 to 40 minutes. Use it for fence and mailbox posts, flag poles, playground equipment, and lamp and sign posts. Heavy objects, such as basketball backboards, may be hung from the post in 4 hours. (Note: If temperature is below 72 degrees, additional time for curing will be required.)

Pour mix dry from the bag into the hole until it reaches 3 to 4 inches from the top. Pour water onto the dry mix and allow it to soak in. Fill the remainder of the hole with soil dug from the hole. Use at least one gallon of water for each 50-pound bag of mix.

Fast-Setting Concrete Mix is also ideal for constructing piers, pillars, footers and slabs 2″ or thicker when pre-mixed with water to a 2-3 inch slump. Initial set occurs in 20-40 minutes with walk-on time of 2 hours unless the temperature is below 72 degrees, when additional time for curing will be required.

QUIKRETE® 5000 High Early Strength Concrete Mix. QUIKRETE® 5000 is the ideal choice for any concrete use requiring high early strength. It is designed to produce faster strength gains and improved workability. QUIKRETE® 5000 gains strength quickly, making it ideal for cold weather applications.

QUIKRETE® Sand Mix (Fine Topping). This all-purpose mixture of cement and fine sand is designed for jobs where concrete is needed in less than a 2″ thickness. Sand mix cures to a stronger finish than ordinary concrete because of its higher cement content. It can also be used for filling cracks, resurfacing, stuccoing, grouting drain tile, and laying flagstone and paving bricks. A 60-pound bag yields approximately a half cubic foot; see page 189 for further information regarding yield.

QUIKRETE® Mortar Mix (Masonry). This mix simplifies mixing mortar for laying brick, block, or stone. A blend of masonry-type cement and graded sands, QUIKRETE® Mortar Mix can also be used for repairing and tuck-pointing existing masonry walls and surfaces. A 60-pound bag will lay approximately 30 bricks or 11 concrete blocks (3/8″ joints); see page 190 for further information regarding yield.

QUIKRETE® Mason Mix. Mason Mix is a commercial-grade blend of sand and cements specially selected for masonry applications. It can be used for laying brick, block, or stone, or for any project requiring mortar.

QUIKRETE® Glass Block Mortar. This mortar is used for laying glass block for both interior and exterior walls, partitions, and window treatments. It is also excellent for tuck-pointing, stuccowork, or other jobs where decorative white mortar is required. QUIKRETE® Glass Block Mortar is made of a uniformly blended mixture of white sand, cement, lime, and chemical additives. Pre-blending eliminates the need for dry mixing; and the uniform aggregate size makes mixing, handling, and finishing easy.

This mortar meets and exceeds ASTM designation C-270 for Type S mortar. It is packed in 50-pound multi-walled bags. To lay up to 100 square feet of 6″ glass block, 10 bags of mortar are needed. With 8″ block, 7 bags are required. Twelve-inch block requires 5 bags per 100 square feet.

QUIKRETE® repair products.

QUIKRETE® Repair Products and Grouts

There's a QUIKRETE® product for virtually every type of concrete repair.

QUIKRETE® Vinyl Concrete Patcher. A blend of vinyl resins, very fine sand, and portland cement, QUIKRETE® Vinyl Concrete Patcher is a truly versatile product. Just add water to mix a completely self-bonding material that is suitable for use both indoors and outdoors. Use it to patch cracks in foundations, walks, slabs, and stucco. Vinyl patcher is also excellent as a "tuck-pointing mortar" and is easily shaped to repair chipped edges on steps, ledges, and cast concrete. Vinyl patcher also protects against radon infiltration. It is as durable and tough as acrylics and can be featheredged to 1/16″ thickness. A 40-pound bag will repair an area of approximately 20 square feet to a 1/4″ depth.

QUIKRETE® Quick-Setting Cement. This mix is specially formulated to reach its initial set in 5 to 10 minutes so it can be sculpted during application and retempered when necessary. Use it for making repairs where rapid initial setting and high final strength are needed, such as on damaged swimming pools, septic tanks, retaining walls, precast concrete pipe, well covers, culverts, curbing, and other concrete units such as birdbaths, sundials, etc. Seven pounds of cement will yield approximately 100 cubic inches.

QUIKRETE® Anchoring Cement. QUIKRETE® Anchoring Cement expands as it hardens to become stronger than concrete. After adding water, it pours like syrup and sets hard in 10 to 30 minutes. Use it for setting bolts, posts, handrails, machinery, fences, columns, and almost anything else to be anchored in concrete. When used outdoors, coat anchoring cement surfaces with a waterproofing masonry sealant. Six pounds of cement yield approximately 86 cubic inches.

QUIKRETE® Concrete & Asphalt Cleaner. This is a strong, acid-free, all-purpose cleaner for removing oil, grease, or soil buildup from concrete, asphalt, or any other hard surface where water can be used. Use it for brick, slate, quarry tiles, even tools and lawnmowers. QUIKRETE® Concrete & Asphalt Cleaner should also be used just prior to applications of TRAFFIC TOP®

Driveway Sealer and QUIKRETE® Vinyl Concrete Patcher. Coverage will vary widely, depending on the surface texture, the amount of dirt and grease, and the thickness of the application.

QUIKRETE® Gray Concrete Crack Seal. QUIKRETE® Gray Concrete Crack Seal is formulated to fill cracks in any concrete surface, including walkways, patios, decks, driveways, steps and appliance platforms. It seals out water and weather and maintains adhesion when exposed to freeze/ thaw cycles. This blended latex emulsion is specially designed to adhere to all masonry surfaces, and its gray tint blends well with the natural color of concrete.

QUIKRETE® Gray Concrete Crack Seal is a convenient, ready-to-use product that can be poured directly from the container. Single applications should be 1/4″ or less. Deeper cracks can be filled with multiple applications. The product dries hard in 30 minutes and cleans up easily with hot water. It is available in quart and gallon bottles with easy-pour spouts.

QUIKRETE® Concrete Repair Caulk. This new, nonflammable acrylic latex caulk dries quickly to a tough, flexible finish that blends with concrete surfaces. Repair cracks in concrete, masonry, stucco, patios, sidewalks, and driveways. QUIKRETE® Concrete Repair Caulk is more flexible and adhesive than solvent-based concrete repair products. It helps prevent water and ice damage and protects against radon infiltration. A 10-ounce tube will caulk approximately 120 lineal feet with a 1/8″ bead, or 30 lineal feet with a 1/4″ bead.

QUIKRETE® Latex Cement. QUIKRETE® Latex Cement is a two-part product consisting of a dry blend of cement and silica aggregates plus a liquid latex bonding agent. When mixed together, the resulting trowelable material is used for overlaying and patching concrete and masonry surfaces in thicknesses from 1/16″ to 1/4″. QUIKRETE® Latex Cement can be used on interior and exterior surfaces. It can serve as an underlayment for tile or carpet or as a finished wear surface.

This mix is packaged in a 5-gallon pail containing a 44-pound bag of Latex Cement Powder and a 1-gallon container of Latex Bonding Agent. One two-part kit yields slightly more than 0.40 cubic feet of material, which will cover 20 square feet to a 1/4″ thickness. Under normal conditions, QUIKRETE® Latex Cement does not require moist curing.

QUIKRETE® Patching Plaster. Water is all that you add to this high-quality patching material. QUIKRETE® Patching Plaster has a retarded set, allowing large quantities to be mixed at one time. This plaster actually gains strength with age and has practically no shrinkage.

QUIKRETE® Non-Shrink Precision Grout. Non-Shrink Precision Grout can be used for grouting equipment such as base plates, machinery, steel columns and pumps where the elimination of shrinkage and precise dimensions are required. This high-strength, non-shrink, pre-mixed product requires only the addition of water.

QUIKRETE® Surface Coating Products

QUIKRETE® manufactures two special surface coating products, plus a stucco finish coat mix.

QUIKWALL® Surface Bonding Cement. This cement-based blend of fiberglass and fine sand allows the construction of concrete block walls without mortar joints. Simply stack blocks in position and then trowel QUIKWALL® Surface Bonding Cement on both sides over all blocks. QUIKWALL® Surface Bonding Cement can also be used in repair and renovation work as a water-

QUIKRETE® surface coating products.

resistant seal and decorative finish over existing concrete or masonry walls. It also protects against radon infiltration. Its high flexural strength makes it a better choice than concrete for some casting projects. A 50-pound bag covers approximately 50 square feet, 1/8″ thick. Special color blends are available.

QUIKWALL® Fiberglass-Reinforced Stucco. QUIKWALL® Fiberglass-Reinforced Stucco is an alkali-resistant glass fiber-reinforced stucco that provides a high-impact, crack-resistant shell. This product is designed as a one-coat stucco applied in a 3/8″ thickness over mechanically fastened wire mesh lath. Lath can be installed over exterior insulation board, exterior-grade sheathing, or concrete and masonry surfaces.

QUIKWALL® Fiberglass-Reinforced Stucco is available in gray, white, and QUIKRETE® standard color tints. It is simple to mix and apply and can be textured in any number of attractive finishes. An 80-pound bag will yield about 0.83 cubic feet of material.

QUIKWALL® Fiberglass-Reinforced Foundation Coating. This fiber-reinforced material provides a protective exterior coating over below-grade exterior rigid board insulation. Applied with a heavy brush, QUIKWALL® Fiberglass-Reinforced Foundation Coating can be used over all types of rigid insulation, including urethane, expanded polystyrene, and pressed glass fiber insulation board. The yield will depend primarily on coating thickness. A 40-pound bag will yield approximately 80 square feet of surface coverage in a 1/16″ coat and approximately 160 square feet in a 1/32″ coat.

QUIKRETE® Base-Coat Stucco. This is a cement-based stucco product designed to be used as the scratch and/or brown coat in a three-coat stucco application or the first coat in a two-coat application. It is manufactured as a complete product, requiring only the addition of water. Available in gray only, an 80-pound bag of QUIKWALL® Base-Coat Stucco will yield approximately 0.83 cubic feet of material.

QUIKRETE® Finish-Coat Stucco. This product is designed for use over portland cement brown coat and scratch coat layers that have been prepared in accordance with accepted stucco procedures and methods. This material provides a beautiful white surface that accepts many textural treatments. Special color blends are available upon request. An 80-pound bag will cover approximately 80 square feet of area to a thickness of 1/8".

QUIKRETE® Additives and Sealers

Concrete additives and fortifiers increase concrete bond strength and workability, as well as seal pores and provide extra moisture resistance.

QUIKRETE® Concrete Bonding Adhesive. Concrete bonding adhesive penetrates pores of old concrete and forms a chemical bond for new concrete toppings over 2" thick. Roughing the old surface is usually not necessary. This product also provides a strong chemical bond for applications of plaster, stucco, gypsum plasters, and similar materials. Depending on the thickness of the application coat, a gallon will cover from 150 square feet to 300 square feet.

QUIKRETE® Concrete Acrylic Fortifier. This water-resistant acrylic resin mixture provides exceptional strength when added to QUIKRETE® cement mixes or QUIKWALL® Surface Bonding Cement. It provides a nonslip coating around pools when used with QUIKRETE® Sand Mix. It can be used to bond new toppings up to 1" thick and also strengthens and seals plaster, stucco, and masonry surfaces.

QUIKRETE® Acrylic Concrete Cure & Seal. This specially developed, water-based formula cures freshly placed concrete for a stronger and more durable finish. It is water-resistant, and protects and seals old and new concrete and masonry surfaces from acids, grease, salt, etc. Cure & Seal dries to a semi-gloss finish. This protective coating also makes it easier to clean up oil, gasoline, and most household chemical spills.

QUIKRETE® Thermo-Lube (Winter Admixture). QUIKRETE® Thermo-Lube provides antifreeze characteristics for concrete and mortar in cold weather. It also decreases setting time to prevent the moisture content from freezing and weakening structural integrity. One quart to one bag of cement at 30°F is about right, increasing as the temperature drops. At 15°F, usually 2.5 quarts per bag will be needed. This product is not suitable for applications where chlorides must be avoided.

QUIKRETE® additives and sealers.

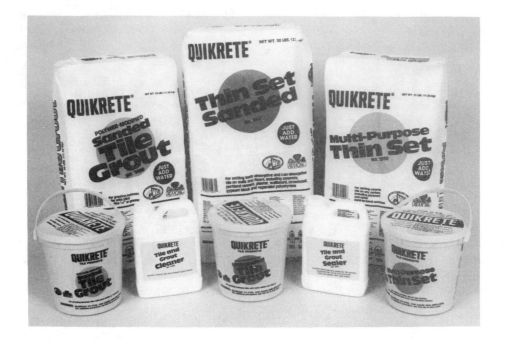

QUIKRETE® tile-setting products.

QUIKRETE® Tile-Setting Products

QUIKRETE® offers a full line of products for setting and grouting tiles, indoors and outdoors.

QUIKRETE® Multi-Purpose Thin-Set. This formulation of portland cement, sand, and special polymer additives is used for setting tile to a variety of surfaces, including hard-to-bond surfaces such as exterior-grade plywood. Coverage will vary depending on the trowel used. A 1/4″ x 1/4″ square-notch trowel will cover approximately 11 square feet per 7-pound pail.

QUIKRETE® Thin-Set Sanded. This formulation of portland cement, sand, and chemical additives is used for setting tile on concrete, plaster, gypsum, wallboard, old tile surfaces, marble, gypsum plaster brown coat, and gypsum block. A 1/4″ x 1/4″ square-notch trowel will cover approximately 45 square feet per 50-pound bag.

QUIKRETE® Polymer-Modified Tile Grouts. The powdered polymer in these grouts allows them to be used with highly absorptive tiles as well as vitreous tiles. QUIKRETE® Polymer-Modified Sanded Tile Grout is used for grouting tile joints 1/8″ or greater, while QUIKRETE® Polymer-Modified Unsanded Tile Grout is used for grouting tile joints less than 1/8″. Both are available in twelve vibrant colors.

QUIKRETE® Tile and Grout Cleaner. QUIKRETE® Tile and Grout Cleaner safely removes cement grout residue from ceramic tile used in bathroom, shower stall, kitchen, countertop, and walkway applications. It can also be used for general cleaning of tile and grouted joints and is an excellent cleaner for removing efflorescence from masonry surfaces.

QUIKRETE® Tile and Grout Cleaner can be used full strength for heavy-duty cleaning or mixed with 4 or 10 parts water for medium or light cleaning jobs.

When mixed with water only, it produces a nonvolatile, odorless solution. QUIKRETE® Tile and Grout Cleaner is available in quart bottles.

QUIKRETE® Tile and Grout Sealer. QUIKRETE® Tile and Grout Sealer is a penetrating silicone sealer for tile grouts, unglazed tile, quarry tiles, brick pavers, concrete, and masonry. It seals against water, dirt, and stains and provides a tough, durable seal that makes cleaning and maintenance easy. QUIKRETE® Tile and Grout Sealer is simple to apply using a brush or cloth. One quart of sealer covers approximately 75 square feet.

QUIKRETE® Waterproofing Products

Freeze-thaw cycles and water infiltration can destroy the most carefully constructed concrete and masonry projects. But sealing with QUIKRETE® waterproofing products can protect and beautify all types of masonry.

QUIKRETE® Masonry Coating. This portland cement-based product seals and beautifies porous masonry surfaces, indoors and outdoors. With nonporous surfaces, QUIKRETE® Concrete Acrylic Fortifier must also be used. Simply mix with water and apply QUIKRETE® Masonry Coating over poured concrete, block, stucco, brick, or stone surfaces above or below grade. This product is excellent for dampproofing basement walls, and when used with QUIKRETE® Concrete Acrylic Fortifier, it also protects against radon infiltration. QUIKRETE® Masonry Coating is available in white, gray, green, and yellow. A 20-pound pail covers up to 200 square feet, depending on the surface and the amount of water added.

QUIKRETE® Heavy-Duty Masonry Coating. A powdered mix of portland cement, waterproofing agents, and silica sand, this coating is minerally reinforced to provide extremely durable waterproof and radon gas protection. Just add water and apply it with a brush; it works both indoors and outdoors and above or below grade. QUIKRETE® Heavy-Duty Masonry Coating can withstand extreme heat, cold, and continuous moisture. It is available in white, gray, foundation gray, yellow, and green. Maximum coverage will depend on coat thickness. At 1/16″, a 40-pound bag will yield about 80 square feet; at 1/8″, about 40 square feet.

QUIKRETE® waterproofing products.

QUIKRETE® Quik-Coat™ Waterproofing Paint. Ready-to-use QUIKRETE® Quik-Coat Waterproofing Paint for masonry is formulated from a high grade of portland cement and special synthetic acrylic resins. Quik-Coat provides maximum waterproofing ability and is recommended for use on all types of interior and exterior masonry walls—both above and below grade. This product is not to be used on floors.

Quik-Coat Waterproofing Paint is ideal for sealing and waterproofing interior basement walls. Added benefits include alkali and mildew resistance, plus reduced radon gas penetration. Quik-Coat also protects exterior masonry such as brick, stucco, and concrete block from harsh weather conditions, water seepage, and staining.

Quik-Coat Waterproofing Paint can be used with potable water on items such as fish ponds, swimming pools, and concrete cisterns. It is suitable for water treatment, water storage tank, and filter-bed wall applications.

Available in 1-gallon cans, Quik-Coat's white color can be tinted with alkali-proof colors-in-oil or universal tinting colors. A good quality latex paint can also be applied over Quik-Coat Waterproofing Paint after 30 days.

QUIKRETE® Hydraulic Water-Stop Cement. This special mixture of portland cement, calcium aluminate, fine sand, and special additives sets quickly (in 3 to 5 minutes) and actually stops flowing water with its characteristic expansion and high early strength. QUIKRETE® Hydraulic Water-Stop Cement is suitable for plugging leaks in masonry walls and for patching concrete basement and retaining walls, cisterns, swimming pools, fountains, etc. This material is excellent for caulking, tuck-pointing, and repairing masonry chimneys, walls, and sills and for sealing openings around pipes and fixtures. It also protects against radon infiltration. Seven pounds of material will fill a 1-1/2″ deep, 1-1/2″ wide, 62″ long crack.

QUIKRETE® Blacktop Repair Products

Blacktop driveways, roads, parking areas, service bays, runways, walkways, tennis and basketball courts, and other play areas all require regular maintenance and repair to ensure long blacktop life.

QUIKRETE® Blacktop Patch. Use this material right out of the bag to repair chuckholes and large cracks in asphalt or concrete surfaces. QUIKRETE® Blacktop Patch is a cold mix of sand, crushed stone, and asphalt and will not shrink or swell, allowing the patched surface to be used immediately. No heating or curing are needed. A 60-pound bag is enough for an area of about 4.5 square feet, 1″ deep.

TRAFFIC TOP® Driveway Sealer. This driveway sealer is a cold-applied coal tar pitch emulsion, fortified with oilproof rubber in latex form. It is designed to protect and beautify bituminous pavements and slabs exposed to gasoline, oil, kerosene, jet fuel, and similar petroleum products. Easily applied, it reduces pavement damage from sunlight and freeze/thaw cycles and covers up to 500 square feet with a 5-pound pail.

TRAFFIC TOP® Driveway Filler and Sealer. This heavy-duty product is slag fortified for added traction and longer life. It provides driveways with 3 to 5 years of protection from winter weather damage and salt corrosion.

QUIKRETE® blacktop repair products.

QUIKRETE® Blacktop Repair Caulk. This nonflammable, weather-resistant acrylic-latex caulk offers excellent adhesion with minimal shrinkage. Use it for repairing cracks in blacktop driveways, roofs, and chimney flashings. This caulk dries quickly and blends with all types of asphalt surfaces. A 10-ounce tube will fill about 120 lineal feet using a 1/8″ bead, and about 30 lineal feet with a 1/4″ bead.

QUIKRETE® Latex Blacktop Crack Seal. This ready-to-use product is designed to fill cracks up to 1/2″ in width in any asphalt surface including driveways, parking lots, and walkways. Latex Blacktop Crack Seal is a pourable acrylic crack filler that seals out water and maintains adhesion throughout freeze/thaw cycles. It dries to the touch in 30 minutes and hardens in about 24 hours.

QUIKRETE® Floor Underlayment Products

QUIKRETE® Fast Set Underlayment. QUIKRETE® Fast Set Underlayment is a rapid-hardening, high-strength trowelable underlayment used for leveling pitted and rough concrete or wooden floors prior to installing ceramic tile, resilient flooring, carpet, or other finishes. This nonshrinking underlayment is for interior use only. It sets in 30 minutes and requires no special curing steps. QUIKRETE® Fast Set Underlayment is available in 25-pound bags.

QUIKRETE® Self-Leveling Floor Resurfacer. This product is a self-leveling, self-finishing interior floor topping and underlayment specially formulated to work without troweling. Use it on precast floor slabs, new concrete, weather-damaged slabs, poorly finished slabs, and wooden floor systems using ex-panded metal lath to produce a smooth surface ready for the installation of ceramic tile, resilient flooring, carpet, or other finishes.

QUIKRETE® self-leveling floor resurfacers.

Simply mix and pour from the container. No screeding or troweling is needed. QUIKRETE® Self-Leveling Floor Resurfacer is available in normal and fast-set formulations. At a pourable consistency, a 50-pound bag will provide 0.50 cubic feet of material.

QUIKRETE® Specialty Products

QUIKRETE® offers many other quality products to help the home mason and the do-it-yourselfer achieve professional results.

QUIK-TUBE™ Building Forms. QUIK-TUBE™ Building Forms are a scaled down version of the rigid fiber-type forms used by heavy-construction contractors. They are an ideal way for do-it-yourselfers and residential contractors to create cylinder-shaped, pier, and pillar foundations for decks and other load-bearing structures. Many local building codes now specify the use of forms for pier and pillar foundations.

QUIK-TUBE™ Building Forms can also be used to create attractive solid bases for exterior lamp posts, fence posts, flag poles, clothesline supports, mailbox mounts, and any other application that requires firm in-ground footing.

Available in 4-foot lengths in 8″, 10″, and 12″ diameters, QUIK-TUBE™ Building Forms can be quickly cut to length using standard tools. These forms are designed to withstand the water content of concrete, but should not be placed in water or exposed to rain or snow before use.

QUIKRETE® All-Purpose Sand. This sand is ideal for use as an underlayment base for brick patios and walks. QUIKRETE® All-Purpose Sand can also be used as a traction material on snow and ice and a ballast for winter driving. A 70-pound bag is about 3/4 cubic feet.

QUIKRETE® Play Sand®. This sand is washed, dried, and screened and is free of organic matter. QUIKRETE® Play Sand® comes in 50-pound bags and is ideal for children's sand boxes and play areas. It is also the ideal sand for building and molding. A 50-pound bag is about a half cubic foot.

QUIKRETE® specialty products.

QUIKRETE® All-Purpose Gravel. QUIKRETE® All-Purpose Gravel is an ideal product for landscaping in and around garden areas, patios, walkways, and tree wells. It can also be used to line fish ponds and aquariums and as a ballast for certain roofing applications.

QUIKRETE® All-Purpose Gravel provides a good drainage base for all types of concrete slabs and foundations. It can also be used as a general backfilling product or as a decorative extension to stucco wallcoating. QUIKRETE® All-Purpose Gravel is available in 50-pound bags.

QUIKRETE® Deco Pebbles and Marble Chips. QUIKRETE® Deco Pebbles and Marble Chips are decorative stone products used for creating attractive landscaping treatments in and around gardens, flower beds, patios, walkways, ponds, decks, gazebos, tree wells, and other outdoor structures. A 1″ layer of pebbles or chips also provides better drainage in the bottom of flower pots or planters.

Since both products contain small amounts of crystalline silica dust, it is recommended that dust masks be worn when opening bags or pouring these products. Pebbles and chips should also be rinsed with water before being used in fish ponds and aquariums. QUIKRETE® Deco Pebbles and Marble Chips are sold in 50-pound bags.

QUIKRETE® Rip Rap Packaging. QUIKRETE® packages Sand Mix and Concrete Mix in biodegradable bags for use in erosion and water control projects. Use them to save time, money, labor, and machinery in the construction of headwalls and embankments, dams, and water-front bulkheads. Simply stack or lay bags in place, secure with stakes if necessary, and wet down to begin hydration. If water is not available, the cement will set up from natural moisture. For smaller jobs, lay out QUIKRETE® concrete or sand mixes in the paper packing, perforating the bags to ensure moisture penetration. A 100-square-foot wall the width of the bags requires about 170 60-pound bags.

QUIKRETE® Winter Products

QUIKRETE® also offers the following products for safe winter driving and ice control.

QUIKRETE® Traction Sand. QUIKRETE® Traction Sand is a coarser sand suited for generating traction on ice- and snow-covered surfaces such as walkways, driveways, and roads. It will not harm concrete surfaces. Each bag contains 50 pounds of sand.

QUIKRETE® Tubesand™. This unique product provides a convenient, simple method of adding traction-increasing weight to your vehicle during the winter driving season. Each tube-shaped bag is packed with 70 pounds of sand. Bags fit neatly into your trunk and can be positioned over the rear axle or above wheel wells where weight is needed most.

QUIKRETE® Rock Salt. QUIKRETE® Rock Salt is used for melting ice and snow on stairs, walkways, and driveways. It is available in 25- or 80-pound bags.

QUIKRETE® winter products.

TOOLS FOR CONCRETE AND MASONRY WORK

The tools used to finish concrete or lay brick or block are few when compared to other types of work. You probably already own a number of tools you'll need, and you can rent, buy, or even construct the others.

Site Preparation Tools

The pickax is useful for loosening sod or soil and for digging trenches for footers. Its broad edge is very useful for working on a horizontal plane when the top layer of dirt is to be removed with minimum disturbance of the soil beneath.

A short-handled, square-faced shovel is best for handling concrete and squaring off footer trenches, etc. A tamper, such as the homemade model illustrated, is used to firm up the sides of dirt forms, post holes, slab subgrades, etc. Finally, a strong metal rake is good for leveling soil or dumped materials.

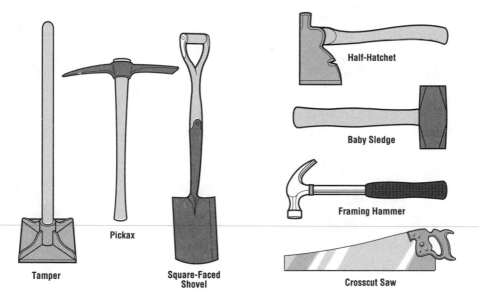

Half-Hatchet

Baby Sledge

Framing Hammer

Pickax

Tamper

Square-Faced Shovel

Crosscut Saw

Site preparation tools.   *Formwork tools.*

Formwork Tools

You'll need a good handsaw or portable circular saw for sizing wooden forms. A 20-ounce framing hammer is best for driving larger nails, and an 8-pound sledgehammer is useful for driving in support stakes and breaking up old concrete and brickwork. A half-hatchet is a good utility tool. The broad, sharp edge is used for pointing stakes; the hammerhead end is used for driving nails and small stakes.

Layout and Leveling Tools

A flexible tape measure, a carpenter's framing square, a 4′ level, a line level and mason's line, a chalk box, and a plumb bob are all essential for accurately laying out the site, for setting up batter boards, and for checking forms, walls, etc., for trueness. If you plan to do several brick and block projects, a high-quality mason's level is a good investment.

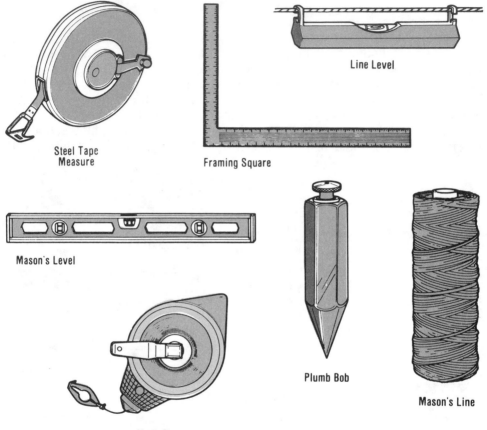

Steel Tape
Measure

Framing Square

Line Level

Mason's Level

Plumb Bob

Mason's Line

Chalk Box

Layout and leveling tools.

Mixing Tools

A sturdy wheelbarrow is ideal for mixing and transporting masonry materials and concrete. A mortar box can also be used for mixing mortar or concrete at the job site. Use the square-faced shovel or a special mortar hoe for blending together the QUIKRETE® mix and water.

For larger jobs, power mixers are by far the best way to mix concrete and mortar. Mixers of various sizes can be rented to fit the job at hand. Simply turn on the mixer, add the QUIKRETE® mix to the drum, and slowly add water. Run the mixer for three to four minutes until the concrete or mortar has reached the proper consistency. Mix only the amount of concrete you can comfortably place at one time, and mix no more mortar than you will use in a two-hour period.

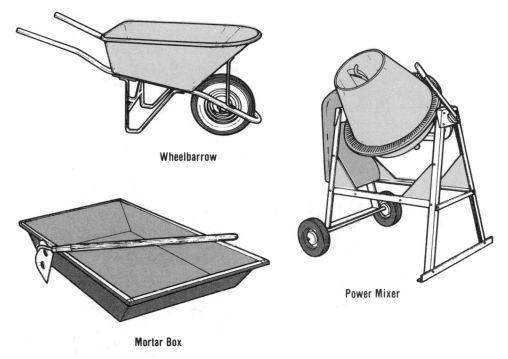

Wheelbarrow

Power Mixer

Mortar Box

Mixing tools.

Concrete Finishing Tools

Screeds or strikeboards are used to push larger pieces of aggregate below the concrete surface and level the concrete to the height of the forms. Although commercial screeds are available, a straight length of 2 × 4 lumber makes a fine screeding board. Move the board in a zigzag fashion, keeping a small roll of concrete ahead of the straightedge to fill in the low spots. The screed should be tilted in the direction of travel to obtain a cutting edge. If necessary, make a second pass to remove any remaining bumps or low spots; the screed should be tilted in the opposite direction for the second pass.

A wooden or metal hand float and a darby or long-handled bull float are used to give the concrete a uniform surface after screeding. The purpose of floating is to smooth the concrete and bring excess water to the surface. Hand floats are available in various sizes and are also quite easy to make.

Work the float over the surface using overlapping arcs. In some cases floating is the only finishing technique used. The result is a finish that is reasonably smooth with good traction. A darby is simply an oversized float that enables you to cover more area and to reach more places without having to walk on the concrete. Bull floats are larger still, and have handles so that you can work extremely large areas quickly. Quite often a bull float or darby is used prior to regular hand-floating.

Hand trowels are made of high-quality steel and are available in various sizes. They are used to produce a smooth, hard, dense finish. Never trowel a

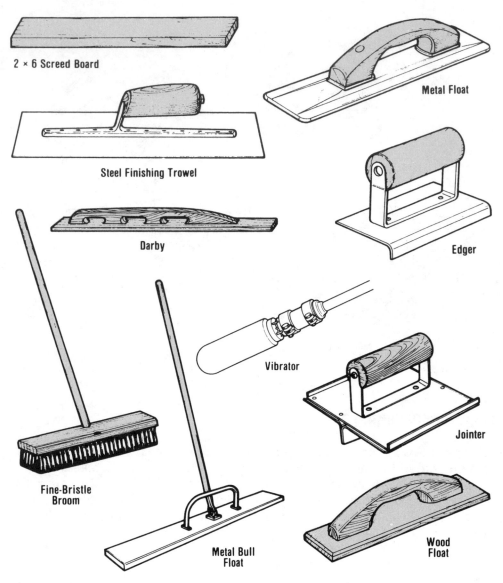

2 × 6 Screed Board

Steel Finishing Trowel

Metal Float

Darby

Edger

Fine-Bristle Broom

Vibrator

Jointer

Metal Bull Float

Wood Float

Concrete finishing tools.

surface without floating it first—water will be trapped beneath the surface and cause the concrete to flake. Timing is critical in a troweling operation; never begin troweling until the surface water has evaporated and the concrete has lost its sheen. A surface is often troweled several times to produce the desired finish. A stiff-bristled broom is ideal for imparting a nonskid, rigid surface to floated and troweled concrete.

Edgers are used to produce a neat, rounded edge on concrete slabs, driveways, walks, and steps that will resist chipping. Edging also hardens the surface next to the form where floats are less effective. The edger is used to cut away the concrete from the form and is then run along it to compact and shape the concrete. A stainless steel edger with a 1/2" radius should be your first choice.

Jointing tools are used to cut control joints into the concrete surface. To be effective, they should extend through a quarter of the slab's depth. Such joints are needed to control cracking as the concrete expands and contracts with changing weather conditions and age. Control joints can also be cut into the concrete using a portable circular saw and masonry blade.

Internal vibrators are ideal for compacting large areas of concrete, especially when the mixture is particularly stiff. The vibrating end is attached to a reinforced hose and slowly lowered into the concrete at approximately 18" intervals along the length of the concrete. In most cases 10 to 15 seconds of vibration is sufficient to compact the concrete and remove air pockets; a thin line of mortar or paste near the vibrator indicates that it has been sufficiently worked. Do not use the vibrator to move the concrete any distance in the form.

Brickwork and Blockwork Tools

Bricklayer's trowels are available in various sizes and shapes, with the largest size being 9" to 11" long and 4" to 8" wide. Select a trowel that feels right for you, but consider that shorter, wider trowels are usually best for the beginner— since they concentrate weight nearer the wrist for less wrist strain. Trowels are used to mix mortar, to pick it up from the mortarboard, to place and spread the mortar on the brick or block, and to tap the brick or block down into the mortar bed if necessary. Pointing trowels are smaller trowels used for performing masonry repairs and tuck-pointing.

You'll also need a mortarboard or a portable hawk to hold a supply of mortar as you work. Remember to thoroughly wet down the board before beginning work so the wood does not absorb moisture from the mortar and cause it to dry out too quickly. The mortar should be kept rounded up in the center of the board and the outer edges kept clean. If spread over the board in a thin layer, the mortar will dry out quickly, and there will be a tendency for lumps to form. Proper consistency must be maintained at all times.

A brick hammer is another valuable tool. One end is shaped like a chisel and is used to smooth and shape cut bricks. The opposite end is usually square and is used for breaking bricks, striking brick set, and driving nails. Wear safety goggles whenever cutting or shaping brick.

Brick sets are also known as blocking chisels or mason's chisels. They are used to make sharp cuts on brick or to score bricks that will be broken with the hammer. The handle and blade are made of a single piece of steel and measure 7" to 8" in overall length. The blade is 3" to 4" wide and is beveled to the cutting edge required. Dress the blade regularly on a grinder to keep a good cutting edge. Always wear safety goggles when scoring and cutting brick, block, or stone.

Line blocks are used to run a line between brick or block leads so that each course is placed accurately. Modular spacing rules and story poles are two professional tools used to more easily lay out and check the progress of brick or blockwork.

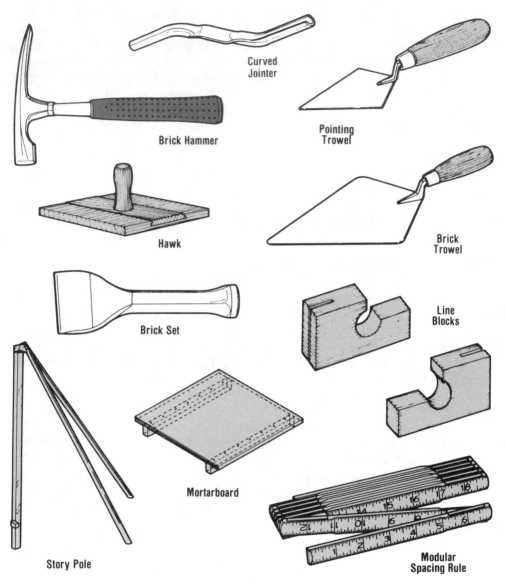

Brickwork and blockwork tools.

In addition to these tools, you'll need the layout and leveling tools discussed earlier.

Tool Care and Maintenance

Wheelbarrows, mortar boxes, hawks, and all concrete and masonry tools must be kept clean and free from rust. Wash all tools thoroughly in water to remove concrete and mortar before it dries. This means you'll probably have to rinse your tools several times during the workday and give them a thorough

Always wear safety goggles when cutting brick, block, or stone.

cleaning at night. After drying them, apply a thin coat of oil to all metal surfaces to prevent rust.

BRICK

Bricks, most of which are manufactured by firing molded clay or shale, vary widely in color, texture, and size. To avoid confusion, it is best to place all brick types into one of four basic categories that are generally accepted by building supply dealers. All brick sold by reputable dealers meets the standards established for the trade.

Face Brick. Face brick is the highest quality brick available. Rigid manufacturing standards assure that texture and color will be uniform and that each brick will be nearly perfect. It will be difficult to find defects such as flaking,

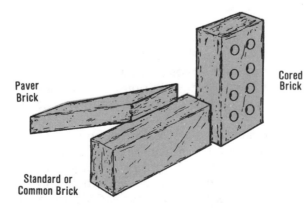

Paver
Brick

Cored
Brick

Standard or
Common Brick

Brick types.

chipping, cracking, and warpage. This brick is commonly used for the exposed face of walls. Common colors of face brick are shades of brown, red, gray, yellow, and white.

Common Brick. Often called building brick, common brick is as strong as face brick but standards permit more imperfections. These bricks do not have special scorings or markings and are not produced in any special colors or textures. Common brick is generally used for backing courses in solid or cavity brick walls and for general building purposes.

Fire Brick. This brick is made of a special fire clay that will withstand the high temperatures of fireplaces, barbecues, stove liners, etc. Fire brick is generally larger than regular structural brick, and it is often hand-molded.

Patio or Paving Brick. This brick is sized for use without mortar joints and is highly resistant to cracking under great loads. It is baked for a longer period of time and, like fire brick, is made from special clays. It is used in the construction of patios and walkways.

Cored brick is available to help reduce the overall weight of the brick. Such coring does not affect the brick strength. Brick is also available with ceramic-glazed facing for easy cleaning in interior use.

Brick Grades

While brick is extremely durable, it can be damaged by freezing weather. The following three grades of brick can cope with various weather conditions:

• **SW** (severe weathering) has the highest resistance to freeze/thaw and rain/freeze conditions.

• **MW** (moderate weathering) can take some rain/freeze conditions, but not severe ones.

• **NW** (no weathering) is good for use in very mild climates where no freezing or even hard frost conditions are possible.

Common brick is available in any of the three grades, while facers are manufactured to SW and MW standards only. Pavers and fire bricks are all graded SW. Your final decision on what grade to use will be dictated by local building codes and climatic conditions.

Brick Sizes

The dimensions of a United States standard building brick are 2-1/4" × 3-3/4" × 8", although the actual dimensions may vary slightly because of shrinkage during baking. Actual dimensions of frequently used brick sizes are given below.

Nominal, or working, dimensions of the brick equal the actual dimension plus the width of the mortar joint. For example, the nominal dimension for the common 2-1/4" × 3-3/4" × 8" brick using 1/2" mortar joints would be 2-3/4" × 4-1/4" × 8-1/2". While common brick is usually laid up with 1/2" joints, 3/8" or 5/8" joints can also be used. Certain brick sizes, such as the modular or Roman bricks, are specifically designed to be laid up with 3/8" joints.

Dimensions of Commonly Used Brick	
Common	2-1/4 × 3-3/4 × 8
Modular	2-1/4 × 3-5/8 × 7-5/8
Jumbo	2-3/4 × 3-3/4 × 8
Norman	2-1/4 × 3-5/8 × 11-5/8
SCR	2-1/8 × 5-1/2 × 11-1/2
Roman	1-5/8 × 3-5/8 × 11-5/8
Baby Roman	1-5/8 × 3-5/8 × 7-5/8
Fire Brick	2-1/2 × 3-5/8 × 9
Oversize	Sizes vary with manufacturer

Buying Brick

Before selecting the exact brick you will use, visit a supplier's showroom and inspect the sample boards on hand. Various textures and colors will be displayed with a simulated mortar joint on a small panel or wall section, with mortar joints struck in popular finishes. Write down the manufacturer's identification number (also known as the range or blend number) so there is no mix-up in your order, and ask the dealer how long it will be before the bricks are available, since some bricks are made only in kiln runs at certain times of the year.

Bricks are sold singly, in cubes of 500, or by the thousand; and prices will vary according to the size of the order. Dealer delivery charges can be quite high, and for a small job the delivery charge can sometimes equal the cost of the bricks. If you can, it may pay to haul your own. But consider that the average brick weighs about 4 pounds, with a cube of 500 checking in at about a ton. So don't overload your truck.

It is also a good idea to ask the supplier whether additional bricks will be available if you run out or plan to expand your project at a future date. Some bricks are made on a limited basis and then discontinued. Finally, if you buy a cored brick, make sure that solid-end brick is available for the ends of walls, windowsills, etc.

A Word about Used Brick

Although used brick is quite popular, you must realize that it may not be structurally sound and that the units, authentic or imitation, can be more costly than new brick. Salvaged brick may have pores so permeated with impossible-to-remove mortar that a fresh mortar joint will be only 50% as strong as it should be. Old buildings contain both high-quality and low-quality bricks, and it is not likely that the salvager will sort them out. Brick manufactured a generation ago cannot compare in quality with today's brick. In short, salvaged brick is acceptable for decorative purposes and veneering but poses an unknown risk when a project must sustain loads.

CONCRETE BLOCK

Concrete block combines the strength and durability of concrete with the ease of masonry construction. The use of QUIKWALL® Surface Bonding

Cement allows you to lay up concrete block and brick without mortar joints. Simply stack blocks tightly in position and trowel or spray QUIKWALL® on both sides over all blocks (see pages 104 through 108 for complete details). QUIKWALL® allows the use of chipped or slightly flawed block, resulting in significantly reduced costs.

Concrete block is often used in foundation walls in home construction and for above-ground walls for garages, sheds, barns, outbuildings, and other commercial buildings. Concrete block is less expensive than other types of masonry; it is easier to build with than brick or stone; and it comes in hundreds of sizes, shapes, textures, and colors.

Sizes and Shapes

Concrete block units are made in full and half sizes, and there are numerous specialty blocks for working corners, jambs, wall caps, etc. Like brick, sizes are

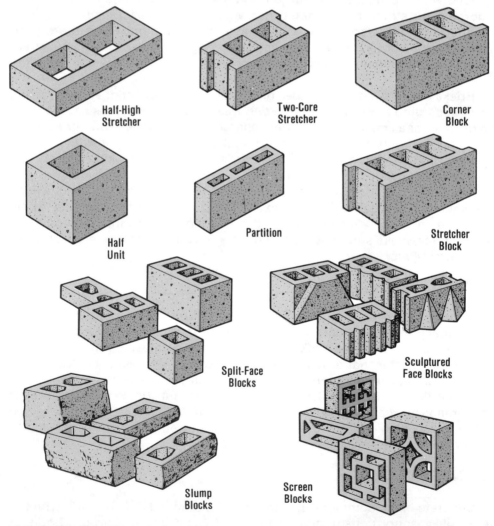

Half-High
Stretcher

Two-Core
Stretcher

Corner
Block

Half
Unit

Partition

Stretcher
Block

Split-Face
Blocks

Sculptured
Face Blocks

Slump
Blocks

Screen
Blocks

Variations of concrete block.

usually referred to by their nominal dimensions, with a standard unit measuring 7-5/8" wide by 7-5/8" high by 15-5/8" long referred to as 8" × 8" × 16". When laid in a wall with 3/8" mortar joints, the unit will measure exactly 16" long and 8" high. Of course, when dry-laying block for use with QUIKWALL®, the actual block dimensions will be used in planning the layout (see page 186).

Standard blocks can weigh anywhere from 25 to 50 pounds, depending on the types of aggregate used in production. Lightweight blocks, often called cinder blocks, have expanded shale, clay, slate, and cinders as their aggregates. Normal-weight aggregates include sand, gravel, crushed stone, and air-cooled blast furnace slag. Most building codes require load-bearing block for foundation walls. Depending on the amount of cement used, surface texture can be coarse or smooth.

In addition to standard block, there are many other modular sizes produced. Schedule a trip to your supplier to see the full range of concrete blocks available. You'll find that some units may resemble oversized brick that is solid or cored and that some are partially faceted so that a particular pattern results when a certain number of block is placed in a group. Depending on the area of the country, the blocks may have different names. Split block has a ready-made rustic facing, and slump block results in a rugged-looking project.

Pierced or screen block can be used to construct dividers or screens both indoors and outdoors. As a patio screen, the blocks provide a good deal of privacy with minimum blockage of air movement. Even large projects will appear light and airy. But assemblies of screen block should never be used as the major load-bearing components of a structure.

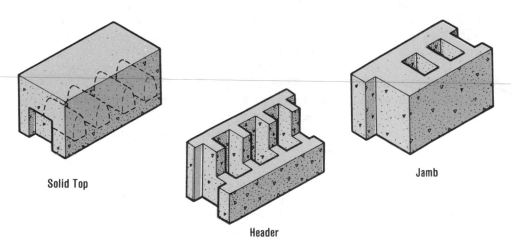

Solid Top

Header

Jamb

Special-purpose concrete block.

GLASS BLOCK

Glass block allows you to diffuse sunlight to dark areas in your home, such as hallways, foyers, laundry rooms, and basements. It can also be used to create privacy screens and partition walls. Glass block admits up to 80% of outdoor light while providing security and privacy. It can distort vision as little or as much as desired, depending on the type selected. It adds an insulation

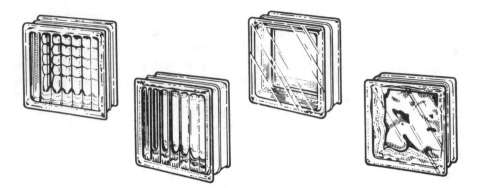

Variations of glass block.

value equal to a double-glazed window and is a good noise insulator. Glass block never needs painting, putty, or caulk. Always remember, however, that glass block is not a load-bearing material. When properly installed, it can only support its own weight.

Sizes, Patterns, and Colors

Glass block is made by fusing two sections of glass together. This gives the block its strength and creates a partial vacuum inside the block. Standard glass block measures 3-7/8" thick, while special thin-line block is only 3-1/8" thick. Square-faced block is commonly available in 4", 6", 8", and 12" sizes. Rectangular block is better suited for narrow applications, such as entry door sidelights. Common sizes are 3" × 8", 4" × 8", and 6" × 8". Be sure the block size you select will lay up to fit the opening, as there is no method of cutting glass block to size.

Face patterns molded into the block are both functional and aesthetic. In many cases, the pattern is pressed into the inner faces of the block while the outer faces of glass are smooth. Swirl, fluted, wedge, pyramid, clear face, light-diffusing, and light-directing patterns are available. Do not use light-directing blocks below eye level (6') as they will direct light up into your eyes.

Glass block can be ordered in almost any color tint. Block can also be tinted to help reduce solar heat gain on western or southern exposures. For increased security, block with extra-thick faces can be used. Solid glass, bullet-resistant block is also available on a custom order basis.

STONE

Natural and enduring, stone has been used as a construction material since man began building thousands of years ago. Stonework can range in appearance from the casual look of a rubblestone garden or retaining wall to the stately permanence of exactly fitted ashlar masonry. And both dry-laid and mortared constructions are possible.

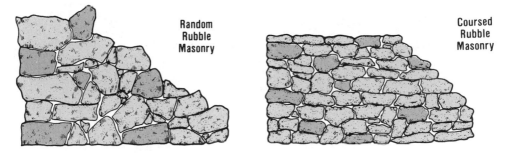

Random Rubble Masonry

Coursed Rubble Masonry

Variations of rubblestone masonry.

Types of Stone

Stone can be grouped in three broad categories. *Igneous rock,* such as granite and basalt, was formed deep in the earth from molten magma and is usually the hardest, heaviest, and most durable stone you can buy. As its name implies, *sedimentary rock,* such as sandstone and limestone, was originally formed from layers of sediment. The composition, texture, and color of these rocks can differ from place to place, but all rock of this type splits easily, making it excellent for paving and ashlar stone. The last major group, *metamorphic rock,* such as marble and slate, was formed under tremendous heat and pressure, resulting in very durable building material.

Commercial quarries and stone yards sell stone in three grades: dressed, semidressed, and undressed. Dressed stone, also commonly known as ashlar stone, is the most expensive because it is cut to specific sizes and can sometimes be ordered custom cut. It can be laid up in courses, just like bricks or concrete blocks. Semidressed and undressed stones are known as rubblestone in many areas of the country. Although semidressed stones have

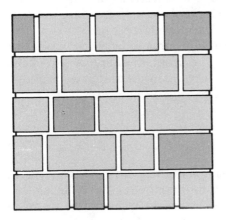

Coursed or Ranged

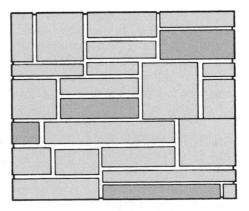

Broken Ranged

Variations of ashlar stone masonry.

Dressed   Semidressed   Undressed

Grades of commercially sold stone.

squared-off corners, they are not cut in specific sizes, and their edges are only roughly parallel. The cheapest grade of stone is undressed because it is neither cut nor finished; it is solid and frequently used just as it is found.

The larger the stone, the more quickly the work goes. Large stones fill most of the area, but the smaller ones fill in between to conserve mortar. Avoid buying stones that you cannot lift comfortably by yourself over a sustained period.

Most stone is sold by the ton, but some dealers sell it by the cubic yard. Required tonnage differs from undressed to dressed stone. One ton of rubble or undressed stone will generally cover from 25 to 45 square feet of wall, with an average thickness of 1'. One ton of dressed stone will cover approximately 50 to 60 square feet of wall surface, with an average thickness of 6". Most stone yard or quarry personnel can help you estimate how much stone is needed for a given project. Calculate the cubic footage of the area to be covered with stone and take this figure with you.

Stone should be uniform in color and texture with a good mix of sizes. If you are ordering dressed stones, specify the thicknesses you want and designate minimum and maximum lengths. Larger stones can probably be custom cut if necessary.

If you have the time, equipment, resources, and energy, you may wish to gather your own fieldstone. Fields, stream beds, and stream banks are excellent sources of fieldstone in many regions, and free stone is often available in abandoned quarries, fencelines, crumbling barn or stone foundation walls, or from building demolition contractors or road excavation crews.

Since almost all types of stone are denser, heavier, and larger than brick or block, building with stone can be difficult. The irregular shape of all but the most exactly trimmed stone can make it challenging to keep large walls plumb and true while still maintaining good bonding.

TILE, PAVERS, AND FLAGSTONE

Like brick, tile is a fire-clay product available in a wide range of sizes, textures, and shapes for both exterior and interior use. Low-fired tile is more porous and soft than the high-fired varieties, which are more vitreous (glass-like) and durable. Most tiles available today are nonporous.

Both porous and vitreous tile are available in glazed and unglazed finishes. Glazes add and intensify color, provide texture, and increase durability.

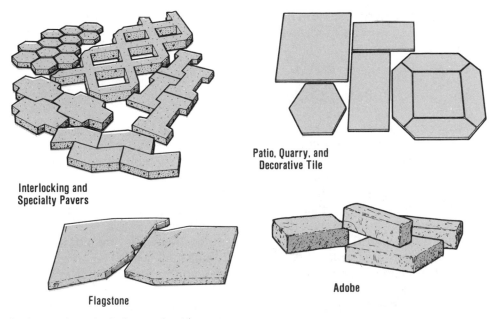

Interlocking and Specialty Pavers

Patio, Quarry, and Decorative Tile

Flagstone

Adobe

Paving products for indoor and outdoor use.

Glazed finishes are most often used as floor, wall, and counter coverings in kitchens, bathrooms, and interior rooms, since wet weather makes them too slippery for outdoor use. Unglazed patio or quarry tile makes an excellent nonslip surface for walkways, patios, and entertainment areas.

Both porous and vitreous tile can be set on level concrete, exterior grade plywood, portland cement, plaster, gypsum wallboard, old tile, or marble using QUIKRETE® thin-set mixes and grouts.

For exterior work, several different construction methods can be used. Paving tile, flagstone pavers, brick, and cut stone can be set in mortar over a concrete slab. Brick, adobe, flagstone, and cut stone can also be set in a sand base, provided the subgrade is properly prepared and leveled.

PLANNING CONSIDERATIONS

Careful planning is all-important in concrete and masonry work. Paying attention to details and working carefully will make the difference between a good-looking result and one that's unsatisfactory. But remember that beauty alone won't make a project successful. It must serve a useful purpose. So the first step is to ask yourself what you want the project to do, and then you can go about finding the best way to accomplish this goal.

For example, consider a concrete slab patio. Its size is obviously an important factor. Plan 20 square feet for each person you expect to have on it at one time. Access is equally important. For a patio to function as a logical extension of the house, you must have easy access to it from an outside entrance. Climate and prevailing weather conditions also play a role in a patio's usefulness. A southern or western exposure may give you more summer sun than you'd like; and prevailing winds, rain, and winter weather may also limit the patio's usefulness.

Zoning and Building Codes

Most communities enforce zoning regulations and building codes, so if you want to construct an outbuilding, attach an addition to your home, or make any other changes to your property, obtain the necessary building permits. This is especially true in incorporated areas.

Building codes set the minimum standards for constructing a project. For example, a code may dictate the dimensions for concrete footings and acceptable methods of construction. Laws vary from place to place.

Building permits are especially important for driveways and sidewalks that cross a public way. Some cities will specify sidewalk grades when a sidewalk permit is obtained. Local codes usually spell out the "setback," which is how close to your property line you may build.

Review the deed to your property. It may include restrictive covenants or easements that will affect what you can build and where you can build it. Finally, pinpoint the locations of all underground utilities on your property such as septic systems, gas and water lines, and electric and telephone wires. Building over these utilities—or worse, striking a gas or water line during the digging of a footer—could be disastrous.

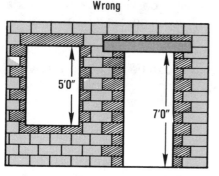

Wrong

5'0"

7'0"

Elevation

Shaded Portion Indicates Cut Masonry

Right

4'8"

7'4"

Elevation

All Masonry Full- or Half-Size Units

3'8"   2'9"   3'2"

4'0"   2'8"   3'4"

Modular planning reduces work time and material waste.

Think Modular When Planning Walls

When planning the length or height of brick or block walls, assign multiples of nominal brick or block dimensions to avoid having to cut or use half-height brick or block. The width and height of wall openings and wall areas between doors, windows, and corners should also be planned carefully to use standard full-size and half-size units. With modular planning, the work will not only be easier but the end result will look more uniform and pleasing to the eye.

To find the number of courses and the number of brick or block in each course, simply divide the proposed wall length and height by the nominal dimension of the brick or block, and then vary the figures until you can divide the number by whole brick or block vertically and by whole or half brick or block horizontally. When working with dry-stack block, remember to use the actual block dimensions in your planning. The following tables will help you estimate various wall heights and lengths when using standard-sized brick and block with typical joint sizes and dry-stack block arrangements.

No. of Stretchers	Nominal Length of Concrete Masonry Walls by Stretchers	
	Units 15-5/8" Long and Half Units 7-5/8" Long with 3/8" Thick Head Joints	Units 11-5/8" Long and Half Units 5-5/8" Long with 3/8" Thick Head Joints
1	1'4"	1'0"
1-1/2	2'0"	1'6"
2	2'8"	2'0"
2-1/2	3'4"	2'6"
3	4'0"	3'0"
3-1/2	4'8"	3'6"
4	5'4"	4'0"
4-1/2	6'0"	4'6"
5	6'8"	5'0"
5-1/2	7'4"	5'6"
6	8'0"	6'0"
6-1/2	8'8"	6'6"
7	9'4"	7'0"
7-1/2	10'0"	7'6"
8	10'8"	8'0"
8-1/2	11'4"	8'6"
9	12'0"	9'0"
9-1/2	12'8"	9'6"
10	13'4"	10'0"
10-1/2	14'0"	10'6"
11	14'8"	11'0"
11-1/2	15'4"	11'6"
12	16'0"	12'0"
12-1/2	16'8"	12'6"
13	17'4"	13'0"
13-1/2	18'0"	13'6"
14	18'8"	14'0"
14-1/2	19'4"	14'6"
15	20'0"	15'0"
20	26'8"	20'0"

Note: Actual length of wall is measured from outside edge to outside edge of units and is equal to the nominal length minus 3/8" (one mortar joint).

Dimensions of Dry-Stacked Blocks

(Standard block units 7-5/8″ × 7-5/8″ × 15-5/8″)

Number of Blocks	Length (Laid End to End)	Height* (Stacked)
1	1′3-5/8″	0′8″
2	2′7-1/4″	1′3-5/8″
3	3′10-7/8″	1′11-1/4″
4	5′2-1/2″	2′6-7/8″
5	6′6-1/8″	3′2-1/2″
6	7′9-3/4″	3′10-1/8″
7	9′1-3/8″	4′5-3/4″
8	10′5″	5′1-3/8″
9	11′8-5/8″	5′9″
10	13′1/4″	6′4-5/8″
12	15′7-1/2″	7′7-7/8″
15	19′6-3/8″	9′6-3/4″

*Includes 3/8″ mortar bed, first course only.
Note: Approximately 56 blocks are required per 50 square feet of wall. One 50-lb. bag of QUIK-WALL® fiberglass mix covers 50 square feet with a 1/8″ coating.

Nominal Height of Concrete Masonry Walls by Courses

No. of Courses	Units 7-5/8″ High and 3/8″ Thick Bed Joint	Units 3-5/8″ High and 3/8″ Thick Bed Joint
1	8″	4″
2	1′4″	8″
3	2′0″	1′0″
4	2′8″	1′4″
5	3′4″	1′8″
6	4′0″	2′0″
7	4′8″	2′4″
8	5′4″	2′8″
9	6′0″	3′0″
10	6′8″	3′4″
15	10′0″	5′0″
20	13′4″	6′8″
25	16′8″	8′4″
30	20′0″	10′0″
35	23′4″	11′8″
40	26′8″	13′4″
45	30′0″	15′0″
50	33′4″	16′8″

Note: For concrete masonry units 7-5/8″ and 2-5/8″ in height laid with 3/8″ mortar joints. Height is measured from center to center of mortar joint.

Nominal Heights of Common Brick Walls Using 1/2″ Mortar Joints

Courses	Height
1	0′2-3/4″
2	0′5-1/2″
3	0′8-1/4″
4	0′11″
5	1′1-3/4″
6	1′4-1/2″
7	1′7-1/4″
8	1′10″
9	2′0-3/4″
10	2′3-1/2″
11	2′6-1/4″
12	2′9″
13	2′11-3/4″
14	3′2-1/2″
15	3′5-1/4″
16	3′8″
17	3′10-3/4″
18	4′1-1/2″
19	4′4-1/4″
20	4′7″
21	4′9-3/4″
22	5′0-1/2″
23	5′3-1/4″
24	5′6″
25	5′8-3/4″
26	5′11-1/2″
27	6′2-1/4″
28	6′5″
29	6′7-3/4″
30	6′10-1/2″
31	7′1-1/4″
32	7′4″
33	7′6-3/4″
34	7′9-1/2″
35	8′0-1/4″
36	8′3″
37	8′5-3/4″
38	8′8-1/2″
39	8′11-1/4″
40	9′2″
41	9′4-3/4″
42	9′7-1/2″
43	9′10-1/4″
44	10′1″
45	10′3-3/4″
46	10′6-1/2″
47	10′9-1/4″
48	11′0″
49	11′2-3/4″
50	11′5-1/2″
51	11′8-1/4″
52	11′11″
53	12′1-3/4″
54	12′4-1/2″
55	12′7-1/4″
56	12′10″
57	13′0-3/4″
58	13′3-1/2″
59	13′6-1/4″
60	13′9″

Calculating Concrete Volume

Concrete is measured by volume, usually in cubic feet or cubic yards (27 cubic feet). Calculate the total amount of concrete required by using the following formula:

$$\frac{\text{Width (feet)} \times \text{Length(feet)} \times \text{Thickness (inches)}}{12} = \text{cubic feet}$$

For example, a 3'-wide sidewalk that is 24' long and 4" thick would require 24 cubic feet of concrete.

$$\frac{3' \times 24' \times 4''}{12} = 24 \text{ cubic feet}$$

To be safe, add 10% to this estimate to account for spills, uneven subgrades, and so on. This additional 10% would bring the total to about 26.4 cubic feet or just about a cubic yard of concrete.

QUIKRETE® Concrete, Mortar, and Sand Mixes are available in three bag sizes: 80-pound (2/3, or 0.66 cubic foot), 60-pound (1/2, or 0.50 cubic foot), and 40-pound (1/3, or 0.33 cubic foot). These are approximate yields that apply in most areas of the country. However, in certain areas, the yields will vary considerably due to the nature of aggregates available to local manufacturers.

To determine the number of bags needed for a project, divide the number of cubic feet to be placed by the cubic foot yield of the bag size being used, applying the following formulas:

Decimals

(cubic feet in bag) ⟌ (cubic feet of coverage)

Ratios

$$\frac{\text{(cubic feet of coverage)}}{1} \times \text{(cubic feet in bag)}$$

In the example above, if 80-pound packages of mix were used, 40 bags would be needed.

Decimals

```
       40.
.66. |26.40.
      26 4
      ____
        00
```

Ratios

$$\frac{26.4}{1} \times \frac{3^*}{2} = \frac{79.2}{2} = \frac{39.6}{1}$$

*Note: In dividing ratios, the calculation proceeds as multiplication after inverting the numerator and denominator of the divisor. Thus, the 2/3 cubic foot yield of an 80-pound bag becomes 3/2 in applying the formula.

When estimating concrete needs for steps, consider each individual step as an individual slab. In the example shown here, the bottom step will need 7-2/3

Nominal Length of Concrete Brick Walls by Stretchers		
No. of Stretchers	Units 8" Long and Half Units 4" Long with 1/2" Thick Head Joints	Units 11-5/8" Long and Half Units 5-5/8" Long with 3/8" Thick Head Joints
1	8-1/2"	1'0"
1-1/2	1'1"	1'6"
2	1'5"	2'0"
2-1/2	1'9-1/2"	2'6"
3	2'1-1/2"	3'0"
3-1/2	2'6"	3'6"
4	2'10"	4'0"
4-1/2	3'2-1/2"	4'6"
5	3'6-1/2"	5'0"
5-1/2	3'11"	5'6"
6	4'3"	6'0"
6-1/2	4'7-1/2"	6'6"
7	4'11-1/2"	7'0"
7-1/2	5'4"	7'6"
8	5'8"	8'0"
8-1/2	6'1/2"	8'6"
9	6'4-1/2"	9'0"
9-1/2	6'9"	9'6"
10	7'1"	10'0"
10-1/2	7'5-1/2"	10'6"
11	7'9-1/2"	11'0"
11-1/2	8'2"	11'6"
12	8'6"	12'0"
12-1/2	8'10-1/2"	12'6"
13	9'2-1/2"	13'0"
13-1/2	9'7"	13'6"
14	9'11"	14'0"
14-1/2	10'3-1/2"	14'6"
15	10'7-1/2"	15'0"
20	14'2"	20'0"

cubic feet while the top step requires 6 cubic feet for a total of 13-2/3 cubic feet of concrete without a loss factor.

For circles or cylindrical forms, multiply the square of the radius by 3.1416 by the height.

For quick estimates of slab and step work, use the table on page 189.

Estimating Brick and Block

To find the number of brick or block needed for a wall, multiply the number of units in each course by the number of courses and subtract the appropriate amounts for window, door, and wall openings. If building a double wythe brick wall, multiply this number by two. Adjust this number if any special bond patterns are being used, such as bull headers to tie together a double wythe wall.

When working with block, remember to determine the number of corner, capping, and other specialty blocks you will need. In many cases, it is wise to sketch out your plans to scale on a piece of graph paper. While they need not

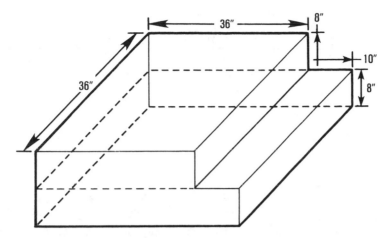

Break down larger projects into easy-to-understand units when estimating concrete needs.

QUIKRETE® Concrete Mix Required to Pour a Concrete Slab*											
Area in Square Feet	2	3	5	7	9	15	20	35	45	50	100
Slab 4" thick — 60-lb. bags	1-1/3	2	3-1/3	4-2/3	6	10	13-1/3	23-1/3	30	33-1/3	66-2/3
Slab 4" thick — 80-lb. bags	1	1-1/2	2-1/2	3-1/2	4-1/2	7-1/2	10	17-1/2	22-1/2	25	50
Slab 6" thick — 60-lb. bags	2	3	5	7	9	15	20	35	45	50	100
Slab 6" thick — 80lb. bags	1-1/2	2-1/4	3-3/4	5-1/4	6-3/4	11-1/4	15	26-1/4	33-3/4	37-1/2	75

QUIKRETE® Sand Mix Required for a 1" Topping*											
Area in Square Feet	2	3	5	7	9	15	20	35	45	50	100
60-lb. bags	1/3	1/2	5/6	1-1/5	1-1/2	2-1/3	3-1/3	6	7-1/2	8-1/3	16-2/3
80-lb. bags	1/4	3/8	5/8	7/8	1-1/8	2-7/8	2-1/2	4-3/8	5-5/8	6-1/4	12-1/2

*Does not allow for losses due to uneven subgrade, spillage, etc. Add an additional 5% to 10% to figures listed.
Note: These are approximate yields that apply in most areas of the country. In certain areas the yields will vary considerably due to the nature of aggregates available to local manufacturers.

be elaborate, such drawings help you visualize the project, estimate materials, and spot any design flaws or trouble spots before work begins.

Determining Mortar Requirements

The following chart lists the number of bags of QUIKRETE® Mortar Mix required to lay 2-1/4" × 3-3/4" × 8" common brick using 3/8" mortar joints. When using 1/2" mortar joints, increase the amount of mix by 1/3; when using 5/8" joints, increase the mix amount by 2/3 the quantities stated.

Concrete block is normally laid up using 3/8" joints.

QUIKRETE® Mortar Mix Required to Lay Bricks*
8" x 2" x 4" with 3/8" Joints

Number of Bricks	30	40	60	80	120	180	240	360	480	720	1440
60-lb. bag	1	1-1/3	2	2-2/3	4	6	8	12	16	24	48
80-lb. bag	3/4	1	1-1/2	2	3	4-1/2	8	9	12	18	36

* In building a wall, approximately 6-1/.2 bricks 8" x 2" x 4" laid with 3/8" joints are required per square foot. In paving a walk or floor, approximately 4-1/3 bricks 8" x 4" x 3/8" joints are required per square foot.
Note: These are approximate yields that apply in most areas of the country. In certain areas the yields will vary considerably due to the nature of aggregates available to local manufacturers.

QUIKRETE® Mortar Mix Required to Lay Blocks*
8" x 16" x 8" with 3/8" Joints

Number of Blocks	11	15	22	30	44	60	88	120	240	495	990
60-lb. bag	1	1-1/2	2	3	4	5-1/2	8	11	22	45	90
80-lb. bag	3/4	1	1-1/2	2	3	4	6	8	16	33	66

* In building a wall, approximately one block 8" x 16" x 8" laid with 3/8" joints is required per square foot.
Note: These are approximate yields that apply in most areas of the country. In certain areas the yields will vary considerably due to the nature of aggregates available to local manufacturers.

QUIKWALL®Surface Coating Products Bags Required Per Coverage Area

Product Bag Weight Thickness	Area in Square Feet				
	25	50	100	250	500
Surface Bonding Cement 50 pounds 1/8"	1/2	1	2	5	10
F-R Foundation Coating 40 pounds 1/16" or 1/32"	5/16 5/32	5/8 5/16	1-1/4 5/8	3-1/8 1-1/2	6-1/4 3-1/8
F-R Stucco 80 pounds 3/8"	1	2	4	10	20
Base-Coat Stucco 80 pounds 3/8"*	1	2	4	10	20
Finish-Coat Stucco 80 pounds 1/8"	1/3	2/3	1-1/3	3-1/3	7
Exterior Stucco 60 pound 1/4"	1	2	4	10	20

*Scratch coats and brown coats are each 3/8" thick. Estimates do not allow for losses due to uneven wall surfaces or spillage, etc. Add an additional 5% to 10% to figures listed.

Note: These are approximate yields that apply in most areas of the country. In certain areas the yields will vary considerably due to the nature of aggregates available to local manufacturers.

GLOSSARY

Adhesion. The sticking together of substances that are in contact with one another.

Admixtures. All materials, other than portland cement, water, and aggregates, that are added to concrete, mortar, or grout immediately before or during mixing.

Aggregate. Bulk materials, such as sand, gravel, crushed stone, slag, pumice, and scoria, that are used in making concrete.

Anchor Bolts. Any of a variety of rather large J- or L-shaped bolts designed to have a portion embedded in concrete or mortar.

Ashlar. A squared or rectangular block of building stone. A wall made of squared building stones in the ashlar pattern.

Backfilling. The process of piling earth against the outer surface of a form.

Base Coat. Each of the lower layers of plaster, if more than one coat is applied.

Batter Boards. A board frame supported by stakes set back from the corners of a structure that allows for relocating certain points after excavation. Saw kerfs in the boards indicate the location of the edges of the footings and the structure being built.

Bed Joint. The horizontal layer of mortar on which a masonry unit is laid.

Block. A concrete masonry unit made with fine aggregate and cement that is shaped in a mold. Any of a variety of shaped light- or standard-weight masonry units.

Bond. The property of a hardened mortar that knits the masonry units together; also, the lapping of brick in a wall.

Brick Masonry. A type of construction that has units of baked clay or shale of uniform size, small enough to be placed with one hand, laid in courses with mortar joints to form walls of virtually unlimited length and height.

Brick Set. A wide-blade chisel used for cutting bricks and concrete blocks.

Brown Coat. The second coat of plaster or stucco in three-coat work.

Buttered. The small end of a brick that has a quantity of mortar placed onto it (e.g., the act of buttering a brick's end with mortar).

Caulk. To seal up crevices with some flexible material.

Closure Brick. A partial brick that is cut to fit into a place to complete a course.

Coloring Agents. Colored aggregates or mineral oxides ground finer than cement.

Concrete. An artificial stone made by mixing cement and sand with gravel, broken stone, or other aggregate. These materials must be mixed with sufficient water to cause the cement to set and bind the entire mass.

Control Joints. Continuous vertical joints built into concrete walls to control cracking resulting from unusual stresses. The joints are intended to permit slight wall movement without cracking.

Coping. A brick, block, stone, or concrete cap placed at the top of a masonry wall to prevent moisture from falling directly on it and weakening the wall.

Corbeling. Courses of brick set out beyond the face of a wall in order to form a self-supporting projection.

Courses. One of the continuous horizontal layers (rows) of masonry that form the masonry structure.

Curing. The process of protecting concrete against loss of moisture during the earlier stages of setting.

Dry Mixture. A mixture of concrete whose water content is severely restricted.

Edger. A concrete finishing tool for rounding and smoothing edges, which strengthens them.

Edging. The process of rounding the edge of freshly poured concrete; one of several finishing techniques.

Efflorescence. A powdery stain, usually white, on the surface of or between masonry units. It is caused by the leaching of soluble salts to the surface.

Expansion Joint. A material placed within or a scoring of the concrete that allows it to expand without cracking.

Exposed Aggregate. A concrete finish achieved by embedding aggregate into the surface, allowing the concrete to set up somewhat, then hosing down and brushing away the concrete covering the top portion of the aggregate.

Face Brick. A type of brick made specifically for covering (veneering) walls.

Finish Coat. The top layer of plaster if the plaster is applied in more than one coat.

Flashing. The waterproofing covering placed at certain points in brick masonry to hold back water or to direct any moisture outside of the wall.

Float. A wooden tool used to finish a concrete surface.

Footing. A base for a wall or other structure that provides stability for that structure.

Form. A parameter or set of parameters made from earth or wood and, on occasion, steel, that contains the footing concrete.

Frost Line. The maximum depth to which frost normally penetrates the soil during the winter. This depth varies from area to area depending on the climate.

Furrowing. Striking a V-shaped trough in a bed of mortar.

Gradation. The distribution of particle sizes, from coarse to fine, in a given sample of fine or coarse aggregate.

Grout. A water-cement, or water-cement-sand mixture, used to plug holes or cracks in concrete, seal joints, fill spaces between machinery bed plates and concrete foundations, and for similar plugging or sealing purposes.

Hawk. A fairly small board with a handle beneath it that is used for holding mortar.

Header. A masonry unit laid flat with its longest dimensions perpendicular to the face of the wall. It is generally used to tie two wythes of masonry together.

Hydration. The chemical reaction that occurs when water is added to cement, causing it to harden.

Joint. Any place where two or more edges or surfaces come to a union.

Jointer. A tool used for making grooves or control joints in concrete surfaces to control cracking. (See **Control Joint.**)

Joist. In deck construction, 2" × 6" lumber attached to beams and ledgers that serves as a base for the deck planking.

Lintel. A beam placed over an opening in a wall.

Masonry. A construction made of prefabricated masonry units laid in various ways and joined together with mortar.

Mixers. Vehicles or containers used to blend or mix the ingredients of concrete.

Moisture Content. The amount of water contained within the aggregate used in concrete.

Mortar. A mixture of cement, sand, and water without coarse aggregate. It is used chiefly for bonding masonry units together.

Pavers. Bricks in numerous sizes and shapes that are used in constructing sidewalks, patios, and driveways.

Pier. A free-standing column.

Pilaster. A projection from a masonry wall that provides strength for the wall.

Plasticity Consistency. A sluggish flow without segregation.

Plumb. That which is vertically perpendicular as measured with a spirit level or plumb bob.

Pointing. The process of inserting mortar into horizontal and vertical joints after a masonry unit has been laid.

Portland Cement. A number of types of cement with unique characteristics manufactured from limestone and mixed with shale, clay, or marl.

Precast Concrete. Any concrete member that is cast in forms at a place other than its final position of use.

Pre-Mix. Any of several packaged mixtures of ingredients used for preparing concrete or mortar.

Reinforcing Rod. A steel rod that is used for reinforcing concrete and masonry structures.

Retaining Wall. A wall that is constructed to hold soil in place.

Rowlock. A brick laid on its edge (face).

Rubble. Rough fragments of broken stone either naturally formed or quarried; used in masonry.

Running Bond. This is the same as common bond, with continuous horizontal joints, but the vertical joints are offset or in line.

Scratch Coat. The first coat of plaster or stucco.

Screed. A long, very straight board used for striking off concrete.

Screeding. The process of leveling the surface of a concrete slab by striking off the excess concrete.

Segregation. The tendency of particles of the same size in a given mass of aggregate to gather together whenever the material is being loaded, transported, or otherwise disturbed.

Set. The process during which mortar or concrete hardens. Initial set occurs when the concrete has to be broken to change its shape, generally about an hour after it is placed. Final set occurs generally about 10 hours after placing the concrete.

Shell. The sides and recessed ends of a concrete block.

Soldier. A brick laid on its end so that its longest dimension is parallel to the vertical axis of the face of the wall.

Stretcher. A masonry unit laid flat with its longest dimension parallel to the face of the wall.

Striking Off. The process of removing excess concrete to a level needed.

Stucco. A finish composed of two or more layers of mortar (white or colored) that is applied to either indoor or outdoor walls.

Tamp. The process of compacting concrete with rakes or short lengths of lumber.

Texturizing. Creating a particular finish, such as brushed, smoothed, etched, or pockmarked.

Ties. A wire, rod, or snap that is used to hold wall forms at a specific separation.

Trowel. A steel tool with a flat surface that causes a concrete surface to become very smooth.

Tuck-Pointing. The process of refilling old joints with new mortar.

Veneer. A layer of bricks or stones that serves as a facing.

Wales. Horizontal members that aid in wall/form reinforcement and distribution of forces.

Weep Holes. The openings made in mortar joints that facilitate drainage of built-up moisture.

Wire Mesh. Any of a variety of types of bonded wire forming a mat used to reinforce slabs of concrete.

Workability. The ease or difficulty of placing and consolidating concrete.

Wythe. A vertical stack of bricks one thickness wide (e.g., a veneer course).

INDEX